SADLIER-OXFORD

Progress in Mathematics
Critical Thinking
For Active Math Minds

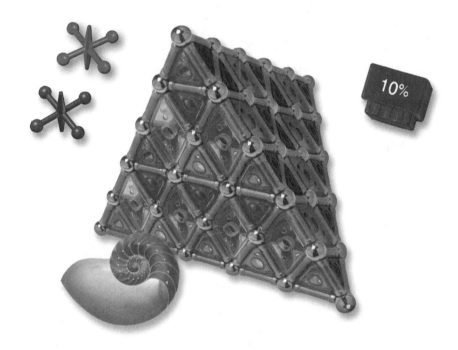

Sadlier-Oxford
A Division of William H. Sadlier, Inc.
www.progressinmathematics.com

Contents

Dear Student

It is sometimes difficult to choose the correct answer to a multiple-choice question test. Often, more than one answer choice can seem to be the right one. *Critical Thinking for Active Math Minds* will help you to make the correct choice.

This booklet will help you use critical thinking strategies. These strategies will help you to decide exactly what a question asks and will help you to analyze each answer choice to select the one that answers the question.

How Can You Build Your Critical Thinking Skills?

There are three different types of lessons in *Critical Thinking for Active Math Minds*. Each of the following lesson types will help you build the critical thinking skills that will lead to success in mathematics.

Chapter-by-Chapter Workshops

- *Critical Thinking for Active Math Minds* has three 2-page workshops for each chapter of *Progress in Mathematics*, Grade 6. The first page has multiple-choice questions and strategies to help you think critically about the answer choices. Look at the parts of a Workshop page below:

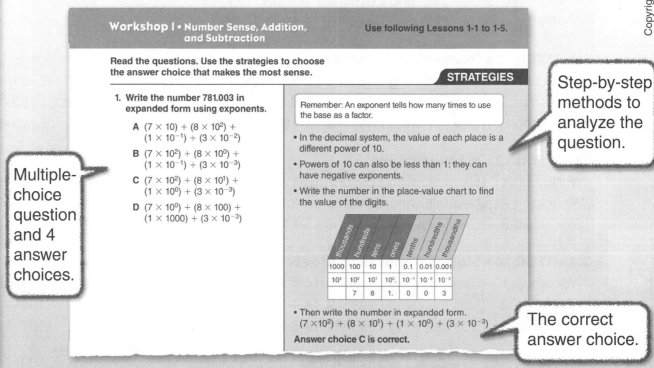

- The second workshop page is your chance to practice your critical-thinking skills. If you get stuck on a question, you can always look back at the first Workshop page, find a similar problem, and review the strategy.

Problem-Solving Workshops

- *Critical Thinking for Active Math Minds* has four 6-page Problem-Solving workshops. These workshops guide you to think critically about each part of a word problem before you try to solve the whole problem.

- Each Problem-Solving Workshop begins with a word problem. The other parts of the Workshop help you to break the problem into smaller parts. Here is an example:

PROBLEM-SOLVING GUIDE

1 Understand the Question
- What question is the problem asking?

2 Understand Word Meanings
- Is there an unfamiliar word in the problem?
- How can I figure out the meaning?

3 Understand How to Solve
- What do I already know?
- How can I use what I know to solve the problem?

4 Circle the Letter of the Correct Answer Choice.
- Reread the problem. Does the answer choice answer the question that the problem is asking?

- The second page of the Problem-Solving Workshop will give you a chance to test your understanding. You will be asked to use what you have learned to analyze and solve a word problem. Remember, you can always look back at the first Workshop page to help you.

- The next four pages of each Problem-Solving Workshop give you many chances to solve word problems on your own. You can use the Critical Thinking Strategies that you learned and practiced in the Problem-Solving Workshops to choose the correct answer to each problem.

Cumulative Reviews: Connecting Concepts

- *Critical Thinking for Active Math Minds* has four reviews that put together the math concepts that you have learned. Each question in these reviews connects a number of mathematical concepts.

- For example, you know how to write a fraction as a decimal, you know how to add decimals, and you know how to divide decimals by whole numbers to find an average or mean.

- This Cumulative Review question connects all these concepts:

Cumulative Review: Connecting Concepts

Name _____

Circle the letter of the correct answer choice.

1. In four football games, a running back gained 6 yd, $6\frac{1}{2}$ yd, $10\frac{3}{4}$ yd and $4\frac{2}{8}$ yd. What was his average yardage per game?

 A 6.875 yd **C** 6.75 yd

 B 13.75 yd **D** 27.50 yd

- To choose the correct answer choice, you need to know that $6\frac{1}{2} = 6.5$, $10\frac{3}{4} = 10.75$, and $4\frac{2}{8} = 4.25$. Then, you need to add those decimals and the whole number 6. You also need to know that you can find an average by dividing the sum by the number of games played.

- Once you have connected these concepts, you can divide 27.5 by 4 for a quotient of 6.875 yd.

We have written these books to provide you with ideas, suggestions, and strategies to help you approach tests with multiple-choice questions with confidence in your ability to apply critical thinking skills to mathematics.

Read the questions. Use the strategies to choose the answer choice that makes the most sense.

STRATEGIES

1. **Write the number 781.003 in expanded form using exponents.**

   A $(7 \times 10) + (8 \times 10^2) + (1 \times 10^{-1}) + (3 \times 10^{-2})$

   B $(7 \times 10^2) + (8 \times 10^0) + (1 \times 10^{-1}) + (3 \times 10^{-3})$

   C $(7 \times 10^2) + (8 \times 10^1) + (1 \times 10^0) + (3 \times 10^{-3})$

   D $(7 \times 10^0) + (8 \times 100) + (1 \times 1000) + (3 \times 10^{-3})$

Remember: An exponent tells how many times to use the base as a factor.

- In the decimal system, the value of each place is a different power of 10.
- Powers of 10 can also be less than 1: they can have negative exponents.
- Write the number in the place-value chart to find the value of the digits.

thousands	hundreds	tens	ones	tenths	hundredths	thousandths
1000	100	10	1	0.1	0.01	0.001
10^3	10^2	10^1	$10^0.$	10^{-1}	10^{-2}	10^{-3}
	7	8	1.	0	0	3

- Then write the number in expanded form.
  $(7 \times 10^2) + (8 \times 10^1) + (1 \times 10^0) + (3 \times 10^{-3})$

Answer choice C is correct.

---

2. **Order 3.276, 4.866, 3.094, and 3.855 from least to greatest.**

   A 3.276, 4.866, 3.094, 3.855

   B 3.094, 3.276, 3.855, 4.866

   C 4.866, 3.855, 3.276, 3.094

   D 3.855, 3.276, 3.094, 4.866

- Start at the left and compare the digits in each place.

  $4 > 3$ So 4.866 is the greatest.
  $8 > 2$ So 3.855 is the next greatest.
  $0 < 2$ So 3.094 is least.

In order from least to greatest the decimals are 3.094, 3.276, 3.855, 4.866

Answer choice B is correct.

---

3. **What is 0.946 rounded to the nearest tenth?**

   A 0.9   **C** 0.95

   B 0.94   **D** 1.0

- Identify the place you are rounding to.
- Circle the digit in that place. **0.9̣46**
- Look at the digit to the right.
  Is it 4 or less? Round down.
  Is it 5 or more? Round up.

  0.9̣46 → 0.9

Answer choice A is correct.

Circle the letter of the correct answer choice.

4. Write the number 10.49 in expanded form using exponents.

   A $(1 \times 10^2) + (4 \times 10^{-1}) + (9 \times 10^{-2})$

   B $(1 \times 10^1) + (4 \times 10^{-1}) + (9 \times 10^{-2})$

   C $(1 \times 10^1) + (4 \times 10^0) + (9 \times 10^{-1})$

   D $(1 \times 10^0) + (4 \times 10^{-1}) + (9 \times 10^{-2})$

5. Order the decimals from greatest to least.

   0.4935, 0.492, 0.4921, 0.4853

   A 0.4935, 0.4921, 0.492, 0.4853

   B 0.4921, 0.4935, 0.492, 0.4853

   C 0.4935, 0.492, 0.4921, 0.4853

   D 0.4853, 0.492, 0.4921, 0.4935

6. Which number rounds to 15,700,000 when rounded to the nearest hundred thousand?

   A 15,000,000

   B 15,579,999

   C 15,649,999

   D 15,659,999

7. A number rounds to 5.68. What could the number be?

   A 5.679   C 5.868

   B 5.688   D 5.658

8. What is the standard form of this number rounded to the nearest hundredth?

   $(1 \times 10^0) + (7 \times 10^{-3}) + (9 \times 10^{-4})$

   A 1.00   C 1.01

   B 1.008   D 1.08

9. What is the number 0.62137 rounded to the nearest thousandth?

   A 0.621   B 0.626

   C 0.6214   D 0.6213

10. Which list of decimals is ordered from *least* to *greatest*?

   A 0.331, 0.348, 0.395, 0.437

   B 0.437, 0.395, 0.348, 0.331

   C 0.348, 0.331, 0.395, 0.437

   D 0.395, 0.331, 0.348, 0.437

Read the questions. Use the strategies to choose the answer choice that makes the most sense.

STRATEGIES

1. Three parts of hiking trail are 13.2, 9.9, and 11.75 miles long. What is a reasonable estimate for the length of the entire hiking trail?

   A about 28 miles

   B about 30 miles

   C about 35 miles

   D about 40 miles

Think
The word *about* tells you to estimate.

• Round each number to the greatest nonzero place of the least number.

$$13.2 \longrightarrow 13$$
$$\text{least number} \longrightarrow 9.9 \longrightarrow 10$$
$$11.75 \longrightarrow 12$$

• Add the rounded numbers. $13 + 10 + 12 = 35$

Answer choice C is correct.

---

2. Diego biked 21.45 miles last week. He jogged 14.7 miles. How many miles did he exercise in all?

   A 35.42   C 35.15

   B 35.52   D 36.15

$$\begin{array}{r} 1 \\ 21.45 \\ +\ 14.70 \\ \hline 36.15 \end{array}$$

• Align the decimal points in the addends.
• Write zeros as placeholders as needed.

• Write the decimal point in the sum.

Answer choice D is correct.

---

3. Find the difference.

   $$31.45 - 15.7$$

   A 15.75   C 17.75

   B 7.38   D 16.75

You can follow these steps to subtract $31.75 - 15.7$.

$$\begin{array}{r} 31.45 \\ -\ 15.70 \\ \hline \end{array}$$

• Align the decimal points.
• Use zeros as placeholders as needed.

$$\begin{array}{r} 31.45 \\ -\ 15.70 \\ \hline 20. \end{array}$$

• Use front-end estimation.
• Subtract the front digits.
• Write zeros for the other digits in the whole-number part of the number.

Subtract to find the exact difference.

$$\begin{array}{r} {\scriptstyle 10} \\ {\scriptstyle 2\,0\,14} \\ 3\!\!\!/1.\!\!\!/45 \\ -\ 15.70 \\ \hline 15.75 \end{array}$$

Regroup if necessary.

Write the decimal point in the difference.

$15.75 \approx 20.$ The answer is reasonable.

> Remember: $\approx$ means "is about equal to."

Answer choice A is correct.

Circle the letter of the correct answer choice.

4. This bill shows what Ella spent on office supplies. Use rounding to find the most reasonable estimate for the total amount that she spent.

XYZ Office Supply	
pencils	$ 7.25
paper	$55.28
paperclips	$ 9.50

A about $72 **C** about $77

B about $74 **D** about $80

5. About how much greater is the difference of 39.27 and 5.993 than the difference of 39.27 and 1.08? Use rounding.

A about 4 **C** about 33

B about 5 **D** about 38

6. Lauren will add a $15 tip to this check. Use front-end estimation to find about how much the total amount of the bill will be.

Guest Check	
2 Dinner Specials	
2 Salads	
2 Cokes	
Total	$76.53

A about $80 **C** about $90

B about $85 **D** about $100

7. Drake is walking a 22.45-mile hiking trail. He just passed the 13.8-mile marker. How much farther does he have to go?

A 8.65 miles **C** 21.07 miles

B 9.37 miles **D** 36.25 miles

8. Find the sum.

2.594 + 305.1 + 65.008 + 24.7793

A 3.974813 **C** 397.4813

B 386.3613 **D** 3,974,813

Use the table to answer questions 9–10.

Social Studies Grades	
Marking Period	Average Grade
1	90.05
2	88.77
3	91.38
4	85.5

9. This table shows Rod's average Social Studies grades for the four marking periods this year in school. What is the difference between the highest and lowest grades?

A 4.55 **C** 6.33

B 5.88 **D** 82.83

10. Rod wants to find his average final grade. He starts by estimating the total of the four marking periods. By rounding to the nearest ten, what is the most reasonable estimate of the total?

A about 350 **C** about 360

B about 356 **D** about 400

11. Find the total distance traveled by all three cars.

Car	Distance Traveled in Miles
1	13,052.64
2	6,520.10
3	920.70

A 200,493 mi **C** 20,493,440 mi

B 20,444.44 mi **D** 20,493.44 mi

Read the questions. Use the strategies to choose the answer choice that makes the most sense.

STRATEGIES

1. Mark works 35 regular hours and some overtime hours, *h*, each week. Which expression shows the number of hours Mark works in all?

   A $h - 35$

   B $35 - h$

   C $35 + h$

   D $35h$

To represent the total hours that Mark works, you can write an algebraic expression.

> Remember: An expression that includes a variable is called an algebraic expression.

- Use a variable to represent the unknown quantity. In this problem, *h*, is the variable that stands for the number of overtime hours.

Find the expression that shows the total amount of hours Mark works.

Answer choice C is correct.

2. Evaluate the expression.

   $86 - n$, when $n = 19$

   A 73

   B 77

   C 67

   D 105

··Think····
Evaluate means "to find the value."

To evaluate an algebraic expression, you can follow these steps:

- Replace the variable with a given number.

- Compute to find the value of the expression.

   $86 - n$ ◀— Replace *n* with 19.

   $86 - 19$ ◀— Subtract.

   ↓

   67 ◀— value of expression

Answer choice C is correct.

3. Find the value of the expression when $p = 16.8$ and $r = 9.07$.

   $19 + p + r$

   A 24.87   **C** 35.15

   B 34.87   **D** 44.87

- First, replace each variable with the number that it represents.

   $19 + \quad p \quad + \quad r$
   ↓ \qquad ↓ \qquad ↓
   $19 + 16.8 + 9.07$

- Then add.

   $19 + 16.8 + 9.07 = \boxed{44.87}$
   ↓
   Value of expression

Answer choice D is correct.

Name _____

Circle the letter of the correct answer choice.

---

4. Which word expression means the same as $z - 8$?

  A 8 less than a number

  B a number added to 8

  C 8 decreased by a number

  D 8 more than a number

---

5. Casey is reading a 750-page book. If he reads p pages, how many pages does he have left?

  A $p + 750$

  B $750 + p$

  C $p - 750$

  D $750 - p$

---

6. Hannah has \$500 in her bank account. She puts x dollars into her bank account. Which expression shows how much money she has now?

  A $500 + x$

  B $x - 500$

  C $500 - x$

  D $500x$

---

7. There are 37 people on a bus. At the bus stop, n people get on and p people get off. Which expression shows the number of people on the bus now?

  A $37 - n - p$

  B $37 + n + p$

  C $37 - n + p$

  D $37 + n - p$

Use this table of values to evaluate the expressions in questions 8–11.

Variable	Value
a	0.65
b	0.03
c	1.47
d	0.19

8. Evaluate.

$$2.35 - d$$

  A 1.70   **C** 2.35

  B 2.16   **D** 2.54

9. Evaluate.

$$c + a$$

  A 1.47   **C** 1.69

  B 1.66   **D** 2.12

10. Evaluate.

$$c - 1.3 + b$$

  A 0.14   **C** 0.2

  B 0.17   **D** 0.47

11. Jill had c change in her pocket. She had b change in her purse. She used the change in her pocket to spend a on gum. Which expression shows the situation?

  A $c - a - b$

  B $c - a + b$

  C $c + a - b$

  D $c + a + b$

Read the questions. Use the strategies to choose the answer choice that makes the most sense.

STRATEGIES

1. A theater has 1,000 seats. Tickets cost $39.95. How much does the theater earn on a night if it sells out?

   A $399.50

   B $3995

   C $39,950

   D $399,500

• Show the pattern.

$39.95 \times 1 = 39.95$
$39.95 \times 10 = 399.5$
$39.95 \times 100 = 3,995$
$39.95 \times 1000 = 39,950$

$1000 \times 3\,9\underset{\frown}{.9\,5\,0}$

Think

Count the zeros in the multiplier to decide how many places to the right to move the decimal point.

Answer choice C is correct. The theater will earn $39,950.

---

2. Jim runs a movie theater. The theater sold 906 tickets every day last year. How many tickets were sold in all?

   A 35,040

   B 312,690

   C 330,690

   D 360,000

• First estimate by rounding. Use the estimate to select the reasonable answer choices.

$$906 \longrightarrow 900$$
$$365 \longrightarrow 400$$

$$900 \times 400 = 360,000$$

Reasonable answer choices.

B 312,690

C 330,690

D 360,000

Multiply.

$$\begin{array}{r} 365 \\ \times\ 906 \\ \hline 2190 \\ +\ 3285 \\ \hline 330,690 \end{array}$$

Remember: Use place value to align the partial products as you multiply.

Think

Change the order of the factors and multiply again to the check the answer.

Answer choice C is correct. The theater sold 330,690 tickets.

Circle the letter of the correct answer choice.

3. What number is missing from the chart?

5	×	8	=	40
50	×	80	=	4000
500	×	800	=	☐
5000	×	8000	=	40,000,000

A 4,000

B 40,000

C 400,000

D 4,000,000

4. Find the product. $3000 × 43 = n$

A 12,900

B 43,000

C 46,000

D 129,000

5. Find the missing number that makes this equation true.

$$0.516 × n = 5.16$$

A 1

B 10

C 100

D 1000

6. A high school baseball stadium holds 4000 seats. If the team sells out 24 games, how many tickets do they sell in all?

A 96,000

B 280,000

C 640,000

D 960,000

7. A bookstore sells 18 hardcover copies of this novel. It sells 53 copies of the paperback of the same novel. About how much does the bookstore make on the sale of this book?

A $650

B $750

C $950

D $1020

8. Find the product. $307 × 209 = n$

A 1073   C 63,103

B 8903   D 64,163

9. Each baseball card notebook holds 108 cards. Frank has 54 full notebooks. How many baseball cards does he have?

A 5402   C 54,432

B 5832   D 58,432

10. An adult bus ticket costs $8.00. A student ticket costs $6.00. How much will it cost for 26 students and 6 adults to take the bus to the museum?

A $192   C $244

B $204   D $256

Read the questions. Use the strategies to choose the answer choice that makes the most sense.

STRATEGIES

---

1. Carrots sell for $1.85 per pound. How much will 4.2 pounds cost?

   A $1.21

   B $4.46

   C $6.05

   D $7.77

• First estimate by rounding and eliminate the answers that do not make sense.

$$2 \times 4 = 8$$

These answer choices do not make sense:

~~**A** $1.21~~   ~~**B** $4.46~~

Then multiply.

```
    1 . 8 5
  ×   4 . 2
    3 7 0
+ 7 4 0
  7 7 7 0     3 decimal places
```

Think
Count and add the number of decimal places in both factors.

**Answer choice D is correct.
4.2 pounds of carrots will cost $7.77.**

---

2. What is the standard form of 5^4?

   A 20   **C** 256

   B 54   **D** 625

• Which number is the base? Which number is the exponent?

base → 5^4 ← exponent

Remember: The exponent tells how many times to use the base as a factor.

$$5^4 = 5 \times 5 \times 5 \times 5 = 625$$

**Answer choice D is correct.
The standard form of 5^4 is 625.**

---

3. The temperature of the outer layer of the sun is about 6000°C. How is this number written in scientific notation?

   A 6×10^3

   B 6×10^4

   C 0.6000×10^4

   D 6,000.00

• Count how many places to the *left* to move the decimal point to get a number greater than or equal to 1 and less than 10.

6 0 0 0

Think
The power of ten equals the number of places the decimal point moves to the left.

$$6000 = 6 \times 10^3$$

**Answer choice A is correct.
6,000 is 6×10^3 in scientific notation.**

Name _____

Circle the letter of the correct answer choice.

4. Find the product. $0.8 \times 47 = n$

   A 0.376   C 37.6

   B 3.76   D 376

5. How much would a box of 48 pens cost?

$2.29

   A $10.99

   B $27.50

   C $50.29

   D $109.92

6. What is the standard form of 8^3?

   A 11   C 512

   B 24   D 6,561

7. What is $6 \times 6 \times 6 \times 6 \times 6$ written in exponential form?

   A $6 + 5$ C 5^6

   B 6×5 D 6^5

8. The diameter of the Earth is about 8×10^3 miles. What is this number in standard form?

   A 512   C 8,000

   B 800   D 8,888

9. What value for *a* shows this product in correct exponential form?

$$7 \times 7 \times 7 \times 7 = 7^a$$

   A 4   C 6

   B 5   D 7

10. Ken buys 11.5 gallons of gas. He pays $2.799 per gallon. To the nearest cent, how much does Ken spend on gas?

   A $32.00

   B $32.19

   C $32.30

   D $33.59

11. What is the value of *n*?

$$900,000 = 9 \times 10^n$$

   A 5   C 9

   B 6   D 10

12. Which symbol makes this number sentence true?

$$2^5 \square 5^2$$

   A $<$ C $=$

   B $>$ D $\times$

13. The average distance between Mercury to the Sun is about 60 million miles. What is this number written in scientific notation?

   A 6×10^6 C 6×10^8

   B 6×10^7 D 6×10^9

Read the questions. Use the strategies to choose the answer choice that makes the most sense.

1. Susan makes $17.65 delivering pizza. Yesterday she worked 7.5 hours. She said that she earned about $160. Which answer choice best describes her statement?

   A Susan calculated exactly what she earned.

   B Susan found an estimate close to what she actually earned.

   C Susan made an estimate lower than what she actually earned.

   D Susan made an estimate higher than what she actually earned.

• Decide whether to round the factors up or down to estimate $160.

$$17.65 \longrightarrow 20 \text{ rounded up}$$
$$7.5 \longrightarrow 8 \text{ rounded up}$$
$$20 \times 8 = 160$$

Think
If both factors are rounded up, the estimate will be higher than the actual product. If both numbers are rounded down, the estimate will be lower.

Answer choice D is correct.
Susan made an estimate higher than what she earned because she rounded up both factors.

2. What value of x makes this number sentence true?

   $$2^x = 16$$

   A 2   C 6

   B 4   D 8

• Determine how many times you use 2 as a factor to get 16 as the product.

$$2 \times 2 \times 2 \times 2 = 16$$
$$2^4 = 16$$
$$x = 4$$

Think
You can try the answer choices one at a time until you find the right one.
A 2 $2^2 = 2 \times 2 = 4$
B 4 $2^4 = 2 \times 2 \times 2 \times 2 = 16$

Answer choice B is correct.
The number sentence is true when x = 4.

3. A company reports annual income of 4.095×10^8. How much did the company earn?

   A $409,500,000

   B $4,095,000,000

   C $4,950,000,000

   D $409,500,000,000

• The exponent is 8. Move the decimal point 8 places to the right to write the number in standard form.

4 . 0 9 5 0 0 0 0 0

Think
Keep all zeros *between* nonzero digits as placeholders. You must count these digits when you move the decimal point.

Answer choice A is correct.
$4.095 \times 10^8 = $409,500,000.

Name _____

Circle the letter of the correct answer choice.

4. Oranges cost $2.29 per pound. Doug says that 4.3 pounds cost about $8. Which answer choice best describes his statement?

   A Doug found the exact price.

   B Doug's estimate is close to the price.

   C Doug's estimate is lower than the actual price of the oranges.

   D Doug's estimate is higher than the actual price of the oranges.

5. A carwash charges $11.75 per car. It washes 15.2 cars an hour. About how much does it make a day if it stays open 8.5 hours?

   A about $200   C about $1,600

   B about $1,300   D about $2,000

6. Solve for t: $8^t = 1$?

   A 0   C 1

   B $\frac{1}{8}$ D 8

7. What value of z makes $3^z = 9^2$ true?

   A 2   C 4

   B 3   D 6

8. Earth's circumference at the equator is about 2.5×10^4 miles. What is this number in standard form?

   A 20,000

   B 24,000

   C 25,000

   D 250,000

9. What values of x and y show this product in correct exponential form?

   $$2 \times 2 \times 2 \times 2 \times 2 \times 2 = x^y$$

   A $x = 2; y = 2$ C $x = 6; y = 2$

   B $x = 2; y = 6$ D $x = 6; y = 6$

10. What is the standard form of 7.1032×10^5?

    A 71,032

    B 710,320

    C 713,200

    D 7,103,200

11. Erica says that 21 CDs will cost about $180. Which answer choice best describes her statement?

$8.79

   A Erica found the exact price.

   B Erica's estimate is close to the price.

   C Erica's estimate is much lower than the actual price.

   D Erica's estimate is much higher than the actual price.

12. Mars is about 206 million miles from the sun at its closest point. What is this number written in scientific notation?

    A 2.6×10^7 C 2.6×10^8

    B 2.06×10^7 D 2.06×10^8

Read the questions. Use the strategies to choose
the answer choice that makes the most sense.

---

1. Bill sets up 3,192 chairs for a concert. He puts 76 chairs in each row. How many rows are there?

   A 26

   B 34

   C 40

   D 42

• Estimate to place the first digit in the quotient. You can use compatible numbers.

$$3200 \div 80 = 40$$

Then divide

$$
\begin{array}{r}
42 \\
76\overline{)3192} \\
-304 \\
\hline
152 \\
-152 \\
\hline
0
\end{array}
$$

Remember: Two numbers are compatible when one number divides evenly into another.

Answer choice D is correct.

---

2. What is the quotient of 0.056 ÷ 1000 written in scientific notation?

   A 5.6×10^{-5}

   B 5.6×10^{-4}

   C 5.6×10^{-3}

   D 5.6×10^{5}

• Use a division pattern to find the quotient.

$$0.056 \div 10 = 0.0056$$
$$0.056 \div 100 = 0.00056$$
$$0.056 \div 1000 = 0.000056$$

Think
Move the decimal point one place to the *left* for each zero in the divisor.

• Write the decimal 0.000056 in scientific notation.

Place the decimal point to the right of the first nonzero digit.

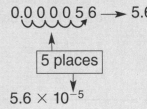

0.000056 → 5.6

5 places

5.6×10^{-5}

• The decimal point was moved 5 places to the right. So the negative exponent of the power of 10 is ⁻5.

Answer choice A is correct.

---

3. Mark will pay his $58.44 cable bill in 6 equal payments. How much is each payment?

   A $9.40   C $13.04

   B $9.74   D $52.44

• Identify which number is the dividend and which is the divisor. Think about where each number belongs when you set up the problem.

$$
\begin{array}{r}
\$\,9.74 \\
6\overline{)\$58.44} \\
-54\downarrow \\
\hline
4\,4 \\
-4\,2\downarrow \\
\hline
24 \\
-24 \\
\hline
0
\end{array}
$$

Remember: Place the decimal point in the quotient directly above the decimal point in the dividend.

Answer choice B is correct.

Circle the letter of the correct answer choice.

---

4. A college football stadium has 19,773 seats. There are 39 sections with the same number of seats in each. How many seats are in each section?

   A 57

   B 507

   C 570

   D 607

5. What is 2.84×10^{-3} written in standard form?

   A 0.000284

   B 0.00284

   C 2.843

   D 2,840

6. A 370.5-meter-high building will have 100 equal height floors. How many meters tall is each floor?

   A 3.705   C 37.05

   B 3.750   D 37,050

7. What missing number belongs in the box?

   $$237 \text{ R } \square$$
   $$41\overline{)9725}$$

   A 0

   B 3

   C 6

   D 8

8. Divide. $15,075 \div 67$

   A 225   C 1,019

   B 235   D 2,025

9. The probability of a coin landing on tails 8 times in a row is about 0.003906. Which answer choice shows this number in scientific notation?

   A 3.96×10^{-3}

   B 3.906×10^{-2}

   C 3.906×10^{-3}

   D 3.906×10^{-4}

10. A dinner costs $73.64. Four friends share the bill equally. How much does each person pay?

    A $15.91   C $18.41

    B $16.41   D $20.91

11. This table shows the number of miles some friends walked each day on a hiking trip. What is the mean distance they walked?

Day	Distance (miles)
Friday	6.9
Saturday	10.2
Sunday	8.4

    Hint: The mean is the sum divided by the number of addends.

    A 3.3 miles   C 8.5 miles

    B 6.9 miles   D 25.5 miles

Read the questions. Use the strategies to choose the answer choice that makes the most sense.

1. Divide. 0.38 ÷ 0.001

 A 38

 B 380

 C 3,800

 D 38,000

Remember: When you divide by 0.1, 0.01, or 0.001, the quotient increases as the divisor decreases.

Think
How many decimal places are in the divisor? Move the decimal point that many places to the right.

0.38 ÷ 1 = 0.38
0.38 ÷ 0.1 = 3.8
0.38 ÷ 0.01 = 38
0.38 ÷ 0.001 = 380

0.380 ÷ 0.001 = 380

Answer choice C is correct.

2. Tara cut a 4.2-m pipe into 0.7-m pieces. How many pieces did she make?

 A 0.167

 B 0.6

 C 3.5

 D 6

Think
Move the decimal point in the divisor to make it a whole number. Move the decimal point in the dividend the same number of places.

$$0.7\overline{)4.2}$$ with quotient 6

Answer choice D is correct.

3. Thirty-two turns of this car wheel cover 48.16 m. How far does one turn of the wheel cover?

 A 0.664 m

 B 1.505 m

 C 1.55 m

 D 16.16 m

• Identify which number is the dividend and which is the divisor.

```
        1.505
   32)48.160
     − 32
       16 1
     − 160
         16
      −   0
        160
      − 160
          0
```

Remember: Use zeros as placeholders in the dividend and quotient as needed.

Answer choice B is correct.

Circle the letter of the correct answer choice.

---

4. Which symbol makes the statement true?

$$3.56 \div 0.1 \;\square\; 0.356 \div 0.01$$

A $<$ C $=$

B $>$ D $\div$

---

5. Julie has 11.85 pounds of beans. About how many pots of chili can she make?

Chili—Makes one large pot
Beans 2.25 pounds
Meat 1.5 pounds
Tomatoes 1 pound
Peppers 0.5 pound
Spices

A   4   C   10

B   6   D   14

---

6. Find the quotient. $4.53 \div 0.3$

A   0.066   C   4.23

B   1.51   D   15.1

---

7. Mike sorted coins and took them to the bank. He had $27.20 in dimes. How many dimes did he have?

A   272

B   2,720

C   27,200

D   272,000

---

8. What number is missing in the quotient?

$$\begin{array}{r} 0.2\square1 \\ 0.9)\overline{0.1809} \end{array}$$

A   0   C   2

B   1   D   9

---

9. A town puts a stop sign every 0.8 miles along a 5.6-mile road. How many signs are needed?

A   0.7   C   7

B   4.8   D   70

---

10. What value of x makes this number sentence true?

$$12.34 \div x = 1{,}234$$

A   1   C   0.01

B   0.1   D   0.001

---

11. Erin drove 148.74 miles on a trip. She used 9.25 gallons of gas. What was her gas mileage in miles per gallon?

A   1.608   C   16.8

B   16.08   D   160.8

---

12. Find the missing number to make the number sentence true.

$$0.026 \div 0.01 > z \div 0.1$$

A   26   C   0.26

B   2.6   D   0.026

Read the questions. Use the strategies to choose
the answer choice that makes the most sense.

STRATEGIES

1. **Eight chairs fit at each table in the school cafeteria. Which expression shows how many chairs fit at *t* tables?**

   A $8 + t$

   B $8t$

   C $t - 8$

   D $8 \div t$

• First write word phrases to express how many chairs fit at *t* tables.

The product of 8 and *t*
8 times *t*
t multiplied by 8

Think
Each word phrase indicates multiplication.

• Then write a numerical expression for one of the word phrases.

$8 \times t \quad 8 \cdot t \quad 8(t) \quad 8t$

multiplication expressions

Remember: You do not need to write an $\times$ in an algebraic multiplication expression.

Answer choice B is correct.

---

2. **Evaluate this expression for $y = 100$ and $z = 0.4$.**

   $$yz \div 5$$

   A 8 **C** 40

   B 20 **D** 50

Remember: **Evaluate** means "find the value."

• Substitute the numbers given for the variables.

$y = 100 \quad x = 0.4$ so $yx \longrightarrow 100 \cdot 0.4$

• Work from right to left. Simplify the expression $yx \div 5$

$100 \cdot 0.4 \div 5 \longrightarrow 40 \div 5 = 8$

Answer choice A is correct.

---

3. **Sarah drove 105.5 miles in 2.1 hours. To the nearest tenth of a mile, what was her average speed in miles per hour?**

   A 50 **C** 50.23

   B 50.2 **D** 50.3

• To round to the nearest tenth, you must divide to the hundredths place.

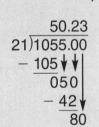

Think
You are rounding to the tenths place. Divide until there is a digit in the hundredths place of the quotient.

• Round the quotient.

$50.23 \longrightarrow 50.2$

Answer choice B is correct.

Practice and Apply

Name _____

Circle the letter of the correct answer choice.

4. Which word phrase means the same as $\frac{d}{4}$?

   A the difference of 4 of a number

   B the product of 4 and a number

   C 4 divided by a number

   D a number divided by 4

5. What is the value of the following expression when $x = 6$ and $y = 5$?

   $$30 \div x \times y$$

   A 10   C 25

   B 11   D 30

6. Divide. $1.495 \div 0.06$. Round the quotient to the nearest tenth.

   A 2.5   C 24.9

   B 14.95   D 25

7. Which algebraic expression matches the word phrase *the product of a number and 12*?

   A $12n$ C $\frac{n}{12}$

   B $n + 12$ D $\frac{12}{n}$

8. What is the value of the expression $5k - (6 \div j)$ if $k = 2$ and $j = 3$?

   A 0   C 8

   B 5   D 12

9. A 4-pound bag of peanuts costs \$2.99. To the nearest cent, what is the cost per pound?

   A \$.60   C \$.75

   B \$.74   D \$11.96

10. This table shows the total number of pencils in 4 boxes. Which expression shows the number of pencils in *n* boxes?

Number of Boxes	Number of Pencils
1	10
2	20
3	30
4	40

   A $n + 10$ C $\frac{n}{10}$

   B $10n$ D $\frac{10}{n}$

11. Evaluate the following expression when $x = 0.4$.

    $$3x$$

    A 1.2   C 7.5

    B 3.4   D 12

12. Harry bikes 16.6 kilometers in 58 minutes. To the nearest hundredth, what is his speed in kilometers per minute?

    A 0.2   C 0.29

    B 0.28   D 0.3

Read the questions. Use the strategies to choose the answer choice that makes the most sense.

1. Evaluate the expression.

$$10 - 3^2 + (12 \div 4) \times 2$$

A $6\frac{1}{2}$

B 7

C 10

D 14

Think
The expression has more than one operation. Use the order of operations to evaluate.

$10 - 3^2 + (12 \div 4) \times 2$ ← First, compute within **grouping symbols**.

$10 - 3^2 + \quad 3 \quad \times 2$ ← Next, simplify numbers with **exponents**.

$10 - 9 + \quad 3 \quad \times 2$ ← Then **multiply or divide** from left to right.

$10 - 9 + \quad 6$ ← Last, **add or subtract** from left to right.

$1 + 6 = 7$

Answer choice B is correct.

---

2. Write as an algebraic expression. Use *n* for the variable.

17 less than 6 times a number

A $6n + 17$

B $6n - 17$

C $17 - 6n$

D $17 + 6n$

Remember: Word phrases can be written as numerical or algebraic expressions.

• Start with "6 times a number." $6n$ is the algebraic expression for "6 times a number."

• "17 less" means you need to subtract 17.
$6n - 17$

Answer choice B is correct.

---

3. Evaluate $5x - 4 - 3x$, when $x = 2.7$.

A 0.7   C 2.7

B 1.4   D 6.5

Remember: Combine terms of an expression that have **exactly** the same variable parts.

$5x - 4 - 3x$ $5x^2 - 4 - 3x$

5 and 3 have **exactly** the same variable parts, *x*.

5 and 3 have **different** variable parts, x^2 and *x*.

• To evaluate $5x - 4 - 3x$, first combine like terms.

$$(5x - 3x) - 4 \longrightarrow 2x - 4$$

• Substitute 2.7 for *x*: $2 \cdot 2.7 = 5.4$

• Subtract: $5.4 - 4 = 1.4$

Answer choice B is correct.

Circle the letter of the correct answer choice.

4. Evaluate the expression.

$$28 + (12 \div 4) - 2^3 \times 3$$

A 6   C 13

B 7   D 69

5. Which expression means the same as *3 less than the product of 5 and a number*?

A $5n + 3$

B $5n - 3$

C $3 - 5n$

D $n \div 5 - 3$

6. Which expressions have the same value?

  1 $6 + 2f + 2 + 7f$

  2 $f + 9 + 4f - 5$

  3 $5f + 4$

A 1 and 2   C 2 and 3

B 1 and 3   D 1, 2, and 3

7. When you evaluate this expression using the order of operations, which operation is done first?

$$5 + 3 \times 4 - (8 \div 2) - 2 \times 3$$

A $5 + 3$ C $(8 \div 2)$

B 3×4 D 2×3

8. A cab company charges $5 plus $2 for each mile. Which expression can be used to find the cost of a trip of *m* miles?

A $2m + 5$ C $5m + 2m$

B $5m + 2$ D $7m$

9. Evaluate $3 + 4k$, when $k = 1.2$.

A 4.8   C 7.8

B 7.6   D 8.4

10. Greg and Lisa compute $(5 - 2)^2 + 9 \div 3$. Greg says the answer is 6. Lisa says the answer is 12. Who is correct?

A Only Greg is correct.

B Only Lisa is correct.

C Both Greg and Lisa are correct.

D Neither Greg nor Lisa is correct.

11. Which is the word phrase for the expression $4 + w \div 3$?

A the quotient of the sum of 4 and a number

B the product of 4 and a number

C 4 and the product of a number and 3

D the sum of 4 and the quotient of a number and 3

12. A movie theater charges $8 for adult tickets and $5 for children. Which expression can be used to find the total cost if *a* adults and *c* children attend a movie?

A $5a + 8c$ C $5a \times 8c$

B $8a + 5c$ D $13ac$

13. Evaluate $7 - 6g + 10g$, when $g = 0.3$.

A 3.3   C 15.8

B 8.2   D 11.8

Read the questions. Use the strategies to choose the answer choice that makes the most sense.

STRATEGIES

1. Solve for n: $48.7 = n + 6.7 + 18.4$

   A $n = 23.6$

   B $n = 25.1$

   C $n = 38.6$

   D $n = 48.7$

Remember: **Subtraction Property of Equality**
When you subtract the same number from both sides of an equation, you get a true statement.

- You can use the Subtraction Property of Equality to solve an addition equation.

$$48.7 = n + \boxed{6.7 + 18.4} \leftarrow \text{Simplify by adding } 6.7 + 18.4$$

$$48.7 = n + \quad 25.1$$

$$\boxed{48.7 - 25.1} = n + \boxed{25.1 - 25.1} \leftarrow \text{Subtract 25.1 from both sides to isolate the variable.}$$

$$23.6 = n + \quad 0$$
$$n = 23.6$$

Check:

$$48.7 = \boxed{23.6 + 6.7 + 18.4}$$

$$48.7 = 48.7 \quad \textbf{True}$$

Think
You can use addition to solve a subtraction equation.

Answer choice A, $n = 23.6$, is correct.

2. Solve the equation.

$$\frac{n}{19} = 85$$

  A $n = 75$ **C** $n = 95$

  B $n = 85$ **D** $n = 1615$

Remember: **Multiplication Property of Equality**
When you multiply both sides of an equation by the same number, you get a true statement.

- You can use the Multiplication Property of Equality to solve a division equation.

$$\frac{n}{19} = 85$$

Remember: $\frac{n}{19}$ stands for $n \div 19$.

$$\frac{n}{19} \cdot 19 = \boxed{85 \cdot 19} \leftarrow \text{Multiply both sides by 19 to isolate the variable.}$$

$$\frac{n}{\cancel{19}} \cdot \frac{\cancel{19}}{1} = 1615$$

$$n = 1615$$

Check:

$$\frac{n}{19} = 85 \quad \frac{1615}{19} = 85$$

$$85 = 85 \quad \textbf{True}$$

Think
You can use division to solve a multiplication equation.

Answer choice B, $n = 1615$, is correct.

Circle the letter of the correct answer choice.

---

3. Solve for b: $18.5 + b = 30$

   A $b = 11.5$ **C** $b = 11.55$

   B $b = 115$ **D** $b = 15.5$

---

4. Solve the equation.

   $$m \div 23 = 6.2$$

   A $m = 142.6$ **C** $m = 14.26$

   B $m = 1426$ **D** $m = 14$

---

5. Solve for p: $73.4 = p - 62.7$

   A $p = 136$ **C** $p = 1361$

   B $p = 13.61$ **D** $p = 136.1$

---

6. Which property of equality would you use to solve this equation?

   $$730 = 5z$$

   A Multiplication Property of Equality

   B Division Property of Equality

   C Addition Property of Equality

   D Subtraction Property of Equality

---

7. Find the value of b that makes the equation true.

   $$\frac{b}{0.3} = 3$$

   A $b = 90$

   B $b = 9$

   C $b = 0.9$

   D $b = 0.09$

---

8. Ursula has some amount of money in her bank account. She takes out $20 and has $15 left. Which equation will find how much Ursula had in the account before she took money out?

   A $d + 20 = 15$

   B $20 - d = 15$

   C $d - 20 = 15$

   D $15 - d = 20$

---

9. Which equation means the same as *14 equals the quotient of a number and 7*?

   A $\frac{14}{n} = 7$

   B $\frac{14}{7} = n$

   C $\frac{n}{14} = 7$

   D $\frac{n}{7} = 14$

---

10. Pilar had a box of pencils. She gave 13 to her sister and brother. Now she has 23 pencils. Which equation would you use to find how many were in the box?

   A $p - 13 = 23$

   B $23 - p = 13$

   C $p + 13 = 23$

   D $13 - p = 23$

Read the questions. Use the strategies to choose the answer choice that makes the most sense.

1. **Find the perimeter of a rectangle whose width is 22 ft and length is 44 ft.**

   A 3.25 ft

   B 52 ft

   C 66 ft

   D 132 ft

Remember: A formula is a rule describing a mathematical relationship of two or more quantities.

You can use a formula to find the perimeter of the rectangle.

Think
Perimeter formula
Perimeter = twice the sum of length and width
$$P = 2(\ell + w)$$

- Write the formula that will solve the problem.
$$P = 2(\ell + w)$$

- Substitute the numbers given in the problem.
$$P = 2(22 + 44)$$

- Solve for the unknown variable.
$$P = 2 \times 66$$
$$P = 132 \text{ ft}$$

The perimeter of the rectangle is 132 ft.

Answer choice D is correct.

2. **Find the distance traveled by a runner who averages 5 mi /hr for 4 hours.**

   A 8 miles

   B 12 miles

   C 20 miles

   D 24 miles

To find how far the runner traveled, you can use the distance formula.

Think
Distance formula
Distance = rate × time
$$d \quad = \quad r \quad \times \quad t$$

- Write the formula that will solve the problem.
$$d = r \times t$$

- Substitute the numbers given in the problem.
$$d = 5 \text{ mi/hr} \times 4 \text{ hr}$$

- Solve for the unknown variable.
$$d = 20 \text{ miles}$$

The runner ran 20 miles.

Answer choice C is correct.

Circle the letter of the correct answer choice.

3. If Caleb averages 40 mi/hr, how long will it take him to drive 340 mi from San Diego to Fresno?

A 3.8 hours

B 8.5 hours

C 11.8 hours

D 13.6 hours

4. It takes Jim 6 minutes to solve 5 math problems. At this rate, how long will it take him to finish a test with 60 problems?

A 30 minutes

B 50 minutes

C 60 minutes

D 72 minutes

5. Chris hiked 24 miles in 6 hours on Saturday. At this rate, how far can he hike in 5 hours on Sunday?

A 9 miles

B 20 miles

C 35 miles

D 90 miles

6. How many yards of fencing are needed to enclose a 23-yd-long and 14-yd-wide garden?

A 37 yd

B 74 yd

C 84 yd

D 148 yd

Use this formula to answer questions 7 and 8.

> **Volume Formula:**
>
> **Volume = length × width × height**
>
> $V \ = \ \ell \ \times \ w \ \times \ h$

7. What is the missing dimension?

$V = 4928 \text{ ft}^3, \ell \underline{\quad} \text{ ft}, w = 2 \text{ ft}, h = 44 \text{ ft}$

A 44 ft   C 56 ft

B 48 ft   D 112 ft

8. Solve for height, h, when $V = 120 \text{ m}^3$, $\ell = 6 \text{ m}$, and $w = 5 \text{ m}$.

A 40 m   C 131 m³

B 30 m   D 4 m

9. Find the perimeter of a rectangle with a length of 11 cm and a width of 8 cm.

A 19 cm

B 38 cm

C 88 cm

D 152 cm

10. A bus traveled at a rate of 65 miles per hour. If the bus traveled a distance of 780 miles, how long did it take the bus to travel this distance?

A 8 hours

B 12 hours

C 18 hours

D 20 hours

Read the problem. Use the Problem-Solving Guide
below to help you think about the answer choices.

Top's health food store purchases 9 pounds of organic pears for
$1.20 per pound. If the manager sells those pears for $1.89 per
pound, what will be the store's net proceeds?

A $6.21   **C** $17.01

B $10.80   **D** $27.81

PROBLEM-SOLVING GUIDE

1 Understand the Question

- The question is asking you to find the answer choice that shows the net proceeds the store will receive selling organic pears.

- Each answer choice shows a money or dollar amount.

2 Understand Word Meanings

- *Net* and *proceeds* are multiple-meaning words.

- *Net* can mean "a tool for catching something, such as butterflies" or it can mean "the amount left after the initial cost." In this problem, *net* means total dollar profits the store will get in return after deducting or subtracting the initial cost.

- *Proceeds* can mean "to move along" or "revenue, income or earnings." In this problem, *proceeds* means earnings.

3 Understand How to Solve

- Reread the question if you need to.

- First, identify what you know:
  - the purchased price for 1 pound of pears: $1.20
  - the number of pounds bought to sell: 9
  - the selling price for 1 pound of pears: $1.89

- Then, choose the operations you will use to solve: multiplication and subtraction.

- Multiply the number of pounds by the purchased cost per pound: $1.20 × 9 = $10.80

- Multiply the same number of pounds by the selling price per pound: $1.89 × 9 = $17.01

- Subtract the *purchased cost* from the *expected sale dollars*.
  $17.01 − $10.80 = **$6.21**

> Remember: Add the number of decimal places in each factor to find the *total* number of decimal places in the product.

4 Circle the Letter of the Correct Answer Choice.

Choice A is correct. The net proceeds for the 9 pounds of pears will be $6.21.

Name _____

Circle the letter of the correct answer choice.

Dawn worked for $3\frac{1}{2}$ hours. She earned a total of $38.85. What is her hourly pay?

A $10.11   **C** $35.35

B $11.10   **D** $42.35

Complete each sentence.

1 **Understand the Question**

• Dawn worked for _____ hours. She earned a total of $_____.

• The question is asking you to find the answer choice that tells _____.

• The answer choices are each _____ .

---

2 **Understand Word Meanings: hourly**

• You know the meaning of the root word: **hour**.

• You know that the ending –**ly** means "every."

• Write what you think **hourly** means. _____

---

3 **Understand How to Solve**

• Reread the _____ if you need to.

• First, choose the correct operation: _____ .

• Convert or change the fraction $3\frac{1}{2}$ to (a) _____ .

• Then, set up the problem and divide.

$$3.5\overline{)\$38.85} \quad \begin{array}{r} \$\ 11.10 \end{array}$$

---

4 **Circle the Letter of the Correct Answer Choice.**

Answer choice B is correct. Dawn's hourly pay is _____ .

Name _____

Circle the letter of the correct answer choice.

1. Brian writes these digits on separate cards: 4, 1, 2, 9, 3, 6. He can arrange the cards in any order. What is the *greatest* number he can make?

   A 946,312   **C** 964,312

   B 946,321   **D** 964,321

2. Leah counted the bills in her cash drawer at the bank. She had 4 ten-dollar bills, 9 one-dollar bills, and 7 bundles of 10 one hundred-dollar bills. What was the total amount?

   A $749   **C** $7,049

   B $4,097   **D** $7,490

3. How many light years from the Sun is Planet Y?

Distance from the Sun	
Planet X	10^5 light years
Planet Y	10^2 light years
Planet Z	10^4 light years

   A 2   **C** 1,000

   B 100   **D** 10,000

4. What is the best estimate of the cost of this dinner?

   A about $19   **C** about $27

   B about $25   **D** about $29

5. Connie makes beaded necklaces. She puts 12 beads on each one. Each bead costs $.25. Which expression shows how much it costs to make each necklace?

   A 12 + $.25

   B 12 − $.25

   C 12 × $.25

   D 12 ÷ $.25

6. Manny paid $48.75 for a shirt and a pair of shoes. If the shirt cost $29.99, how much did the shoes cost?

   A $18.76   **C** $19.86

   B $21.24   **D** $78.74

7. Jeanne tracked the growth of a plant over 6 months. Between which two months did the plant grow 0.6 cm?

   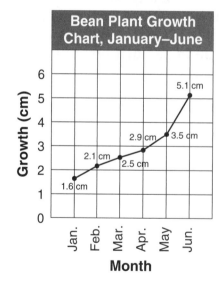

   A January and February

   B February and March

   C April and May

   D May and June

Problem Solving Workshop 1

8. Roger walks 12 miles each day. If he starts on Monday, on which day will he have completed 48 miles?

   A Wednesday   **C** Friday

   B Thursday   **D** Saturday

9. Mrs. Filson's class held a fundraiser. The students sold 105 pens for $2.19 each. What is the best estimate for how much money they made?

   A about $200   **C** about $300

   B about $250   **D** about $400

10. Northeast Electric Company provides electricity to 50,000 homes. During a recent thunderstorm, 20,000 homes lost power. Which choice shows the number of homes that lost power?

    A 5×10^4 **C** 2×10^5

    B 3×10^4 **D** 2×10^4

11. At G&R Office Store, erasers cost $0.29 each. Jim's Office Supply sells 10 erasers for $3.00. Where is the best buy on a purchase of 1 eraser?

    A G&R, by $0.01

    B G&R, by $0.10

    C Jim's, by $0.01

    D Jim's, by $0.29

12. Bill uses 8 gallons of gas each week. Gas costs $3.24 per gallon. Of these whole dollar amounts, what is the *least* amount of money that will cover his gas costs for the week?

    A $23

    B $24

    C $25

    D $26

13. Which choice at the grocery store will cost the *most* for one pound?

    A 4 lbs apples at $2.15 lb

    B 3 lbs pears at $1.88 lb

    C 2 lbs bananas at $4.15 lb

    D 4 lbs oranges at $1.15 lb

14. There are 196 students in the 6th grade at Barker Elementary. If there are 28 students in each class, how many classes are there?

    A 7

    B 70

    C 168

    D 224

Circle the letter of the correct answer choice.

15. Five friends have dinner. If the total bill is *n*, which expression determines each person's equal share?

    A $n - 5$

    B $n \times 5$

    C $5 \div n$

    D $n \div 5$

16. Jack is having a dinner party for 155 guests. Eight guests will fit at each table. How many tables should he set?

    A 18   **C** 20

    B 19   **D** 21

17. Vincent buys paper in the 100-sheet pack, what is the price per sheet?

Paper for Sale	
Number of Sheets	Price per Pack
1 sheet	$0.09
10 sheets	$0.89
100 sheets	$7.90
1000 sheets	$80.00

    A $0.09   **C** $0.08

    B $0.089   **D** $0.079

18. A town averaged 0.5 cm of rain a day over a period of time last winter. The total rainfall was 18 cm. For how many days was the rainfall measured?

    A 9   **C** 27

    B 18.5   **D** 36

19. What is the missing number in the pattern?

    2.164, 2.064, _____, 1.864, 1.764

    A 2.964   **C** 2.063

    B 2.163   **D** 1.964

20. The difference between a number squared and the same number cubed is 4. What is the number?

    A 1   **C** 3

    B 2   **D** 4

21. Jerry laid new tiles in his kitchen. He installed 22 rows, with 17 tiles in each row. He had 14 tiles left over. How many tiles did Jerry start with?

    A 308   **C** 374

    B 325   **D** 388

22. Brendan is 3 years older than Nathan. If *n* represents Nathan's age, which expression shows Brendan's age?

   A $n + 3$

   B $n - 3$

   C $3 - n$

   D $3 \times n$

23. The expression below calculates the sale price of a shirt. How much does this shirt cost on sale?

$$1.06 \times (\$50 - \$8)$$

   A $41.52   **C** $45

   B $44.52   **D** $67.20

24. Ethan is taller than Leslie but shorter than Margaret. Which inequality correctly compares their heights?

   A Margaret > Ethan > Leslie

   B Margaret < Ethan < Leslie

   C Ethan > Margaret > Leslie

   D Ethan > Leslie > Margaret

25. It takes Robert 22 minutes to walk a mile. Lisa can run the same distance in 3 minutes less than half that time. How long does it take for Lisa to run a mile?

   A 8 min   **C** 12.5 min

   B 9 min   **D** 14 min

26. Keri is ordering a new rug for this rectangular room. What is the best estimate of the area of the rug that she will need to buy?
(Hint: The area of a rectangle is length × width.)

width = 14.7 m

length = 18.9 m

   A 35 m²   **C** 225 m²

   B 180 m²   **D** 300 m²

27. The Evan's family uses 30 bottles of water each week. How many six-packs of water should they buy in order to cover their water needs for 4 weeks?

   A 5   **C** 20

   B 6   **D** 180

28. Here's how you find the amount of wrapping paper needed to cover a box in the shape of a cube: multiply 6 times the square of the length of the side, *s*. Which expression shows this formula?

s

   A $6 \times 2s$

   B $6 + s$

   C $6s^2$

   D $6^2 s$

Name _____

Circle the letter of the correct answer choice.

1. An earth scientist collected five lava samples. The table below shows the measured density or thickness for each one. To the nearest tenth, what is the average density of the samples?

Table of Values	
Sample	Density (gm/cm³)
1	1.4
2	2.0
3	1.7
4	1.5
5	1.6

A 0.6 gm/cm³   C 1.64 gm/cm³

B 1.6 gm/cm³   D 1.7 gm/cm³

2. A piece of copper cools from its melting point of 1084.62°C to 0°C in 100 minutes. If it cooled at a constant rate, how many degrees in scientific notation did it cool each minute?

A 1.08462×10^5

B 1.8462×10^1

C 1.08462×10^1

D 1.08462

3. A tour bus company charges $7 plus $2.25 for each mile a passenger rides the bus. What is the *maximum* number of miles Peter can ride if he has $20 to spend?

A 3   C 5

B 4   D 6

4. Interest, or the dollar amount earned investing money, is calculated using the formula: *Interest (I) = Prt. P* is the amount invested, *r* is the rate of investment, and *t* is time.

How much interest can you earn on $3,000 invested for 3 years at a rate of 0.0425 per year?

A $38.25

B $127.5

C $382.50

D $3,825

5. The Jackson's backyard is a grass field with a brick patio. The shaded part of this diagram shows the grass field. What is the area of this part of the family's yard?
(Hint: Area = $\ell \times w$)

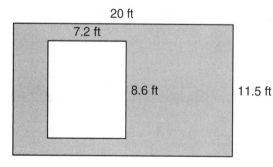

A 31.5 ft²

B 61.92 ft²

C 168.08 ft²

D 291.92 ft²

6. Hannah finished 20.85 miles of a charity walk in 6.3 hours. To the nearest hundredth, what was her average speed in miles per hour?

   A 0.30

   B 0.33

   C 3.31

   D 131.36

7. Which equation has a solution that makes this comparison, $4.2 < k$, true?

   A $2k = 8.1$

   B $5.6 = k + 2.7$

   C $\frac{k}{3} = 1.4$

   D $k - 3.4 = 0.9$

8. The tables below show the value of pennies and dimes inside the cash drawers of two bank tellers at Lincoln Savings Bank. Which coin sleeve has the *most* coins in it?

Jeff's Cash Drawer	
Coin	Value
Pennies Sleeve	$(6 \times 10^4) + (1 \times 10^2) + (5 \times 10^1) + (3 \times 10^0)$
Dimes Sleeve	$(3 \times 10^3) + (4 \times 10^2) + (2 \times 10^1) + (5 \times 10^0)$

Laurie's Cash Drawer	
Coin	Value
Pennies Sleeve	$(9 \times 10^3) + (2 \times 10^2) + (1 \times 10^1) + (6 \times 10^0)$
Dimes Sleeve	$(2 \times 10^3) + (9 \times 10^2) + (7 \times 10^1) + (7 \times 10^0)$

   A Jeff's penny sleeve

   B Jeff's dime sleeve

   C Laurie's penny sleeve

   D Laurie's dime sleeve

Use these formulas as needed for Exercise 9.

   Perimeter of a Rectangle: $P = 2(\ell + w)$

   Perimeter of a Triangle: $P = a + b + c$

   Area of a Rectangle: $A = \ell \times w$

   Area of a Triangle: $A = \frac{1}{2}(b \times h)$

9. Half of this window is covered with a triangular shade. What is the area in square feet of the *uncovered* part of the window?

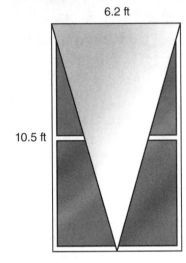

6.2 ft

10.5 ft

   A 16.275

   B 16.7

   C 32.55

   D 65.1

10. 7 less than the square of a number equals 8 minus the product of 2 and that number. What is the number?

   A 7   C 3

   B 4   D 2

11. The area of a square microchip is 0.0001 mm². What is the perimeter?

   A 4×10^{-2} mm

   B 4×10^{-4} mm

   C 4×10^{-6} mm

   D 4×10^{-8} mm

Use following Chapter 4.

Read the questions. Use the strategies to choose
the answer choice that makes the most sense.

STRATEGIES

1. The chart below shows a week of
   winter temperatures in Detroit,
   Michigan. Which day shows the
   lowest temperature?

Mon.	Tues.	Wed.	Thurs.	Fri.	Sat.	Sun.
⁻5°F	⁻3°F	5°F	0°F	4°F	⁻8°F	7°F

A Monday   C Thursday

B Tuesday   D Saturday

• Use a number line to compare and order integers.

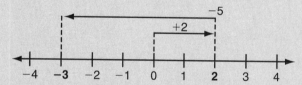

0 is neither positive nor negative.

Think
Any number is less than a number to its right. $^-5 < 7$
Any number is greater than a number to its left. $^-5 > {}^-8$

Answer choice D is correct.

---

2. Find the sum.

$$^-2 + {}^-3 = n$$

A $^+5$ C $^-1$

B $^-5$ D $^+1$

Think
Both addends have **like** signs.

• Add the absolute value of the addends.

$$^-2 + {}^-3 \rightarrow |^-2| + |^-3| \rightarrow 2 + 3 = 5$$

• Use the **like** sign for the sum: $^-2 + {}^-3 = {}^-5$

Answer choice B is correct.

---

3. Find the sum.

$$^+2 + {}^-5 = n$$

A $n = {}^-7$ C $n = {}^+3$

B $n = {}^-3$ D $n = {}^+7$

Use a number line to add integers with **unlike** signs.

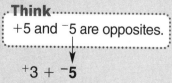

Use absolute value to add integers with **unlike** signs.

• Subtract the addend with the lesser absolute value
from the addend with the greater absolute value.

$$^+2 + {}^-5 \rightarrow |^-5| - |^+2| \rightarrow 5 - 2 = 3$$

• Use the sign of the addend with the greater absolute
value for the sum: $^+2 + {}^-5 = {}^-3$.

Answer choice B is correct.

---

4. Find the difference.

$$^+3 - {}^+5$$

A $^+8$ C $^-2$

B $^+2$ D $^-8$

• To subtract an integer, add its opposite.

Think
+5 and ⁻5 are opposites.

$$^+3 + {}^-5$$

Use the rules for adding integers. $^+3 + {}^-5 = {}^-2$

Answer choice C is correct.

Circle the letter of the correct answer choice.

5. Which value of x makes the comparison true?

$$^-3 > x$$

A 0

B $^-1$

C $^-2$

D $^-4$

6. Find the value of the variable.

$$n - {}^+4 = {}^+14$$

A $n = {}^+18$

B $n = {}^-10$

C $n = {}^-18$

D $n = {}^+10$

7. Find the value of x.

$$3 - 4 = x$$

A $^-7$

B $^-1$

C 1

D 7

8. Which series shows the integers ordered from least to greatest?

A 5, $^-4$, 3, $^-2$

B $^-2$, 3, $^-4$, 5

C $^-4$, $^-2$, 3, 5

D $^-2$, $^-4$, 3, 5

9. Add: $^-5 + {}^-3$

A $^-8$

B $^-2$

C 2

D 8

10. Subtract: $4 - 7$

A $^-11$

B $^-3$

C 3

D 11

11. A football player lost 6 yards on the first play. He gained 4 yards on the next one. What was the total gain or loss of yards on the two plays?

A $^-2$

B 0

C 2

D 10

12. Which variable has a value of $^-12$?

A $^-6 + b = {}^+19$

B $^+8 + b = {}^-4$

C $^+6 + b = {}^+19$

D $^-24 + b = {}^-16$

Read the questions. Use the strategies to choose
the answer choice that makes the most sense.

1. Find the product.

$$^+18 \times {}^-12$$

A 216   **C** $^-6$

B 30   **D** $^-216$

- You can use these rules for multiplying integers.

The product of two integers with the same sign is **positive**. $^+5 \times {}^+5 = {}^+25$; $^-6 \times {}^-4 = {}^+24$

The product of two integers with different signs is **negative**. $^+3 \times {}^-4 = {}^-12$; $^-5 \times {}^+2 = {}^-10$

- Multiply the absolute value of the factors.
$$|{}^+18| \times |{}^-12| \longrightarrow 18 \times 12 = 216$$

Think
$$(^+)(^+) = {}^+ \quad (^-)(^-) = {}^+$$
$$(^+)(^-) = {}^- \quad (^-)(^+) = {}^-$$

$$^+18 \times {}^-12 \longrightarrow (^+)(^-) = {}^- \longrightarrow {}^+18 \times {}^-12 \text{ is } {}^-216.$$

Answer choice D is correct

2. What is the division rule in the function table below?

IN	OUT
12	$^-4$
$^-15$	5
6	$^-2$
$^-27$	9
15	$^-5$

A $\div {}^-10$ **C** $\div {}^-6$

B $\div {}^-8$ **D** $\div {}^-3$

Think
You need to divide the input number in each row by the output number to determine the rule of the function table.

Remember:
$$(^-) \div (^-) = {}^+ \quad (^+) \div (^+) = {}^+$$
$$(^-) \div (^+) = {}^- \quad (^+) \div (^-) = {}^-$$

$$12 \div {}^-4 = {}^-3$$
$$^-15 \div 5 = {}^-3$$
$$6 \div {}^-2 = {}^-3$$
$$^-27 \div 9 = {}^-3$$
$$15 \div {}^-5 = {}^-3$$

Answer choice D is correct.

3. Which replacement value makes the equation true?

$$n - {}^-15 = {}^+18$$

A $^-3$ **C** $^+4$

B 0   **D** $^+3$

Think
You can replace the variable with each value to determine which value makes the equation true.

- Write a statement for each value, replace n with the given value and solve.

A: $n - {}^-15 = {}^+18$, when $n = {}^-3$
$$^-3 - {}^-15 = {}^+18 \longrightarrow {}^-3 + {}^+15 \overset{?}{=} {}^+18 \textbf{ false}$$
B: $n - {}^-15 = {}^+18$, when $n = 0$
$$0 - {}^-15 = {}^+18 \longrightarrow 0 + {}^+15 \overset{?}{=} {}^+18 \textbf{ false}$$
C: $n - {}^-15 = {}^+18$, when $n = {}^+4$
$$^+4 - {}^-15 = {}^+18 \longrightarrow {}^+4 + {}^+15 \overset{?}{=} {}^+18 \textbf{ false}$$
D: $n - {}^-15 = {}^+18$, when $n = {}^+3$
$$^+3 - {}^-15 = {}^+18 \longrightarrow {}^+3 + {}^+15 = {}^+18 \textbf{ true}$$

Answer choice D is correct.

Name _____

Circle the letter of the correct answer choice.

4. Solve the equation.

$$^{-}20 \times {}^{-}4 = q$$

A $^{-}80$

B $^{-}24$

C 5

D 80

5. Which value of *f* makes the following equation true?

$$f \times {}^{-}11 = 121$$

A $^{-}110$

B $^{-}11$

C $^{-}10$

D 11

6. Which repeated addition sentence means the same as $4 \times {}^{-}6$?

A $^{-}4 + {}^{-}4 + {}^{-}4 + {}^{-}4$

B $^{-}4 + {}^{-}4 + {}^{-}4 + {}^{-}4 + {}^{-}4 + {}^{-}4$

C $^{-}6 + {}^{-}6 + {}^{-}6 + {}^{-}6$

D $^{-}6 + {}^{-}6 + {}^{-}6 + {}^{-}6 + {}^{-}6 + {}^{-}6$

7. Evaluate the expression.

$$^{-}2 \times {}^{-}9 - 3^2 \div 3$$

A 17 C 12

B 15 D 3

8. What is the first step to follow when you evaluate this expression?

$$^{-}2[5 + (7 - 3)^3]$$

A $5 + 7$

B $7 - 3$

C 3^3

D $^{-}2 \cdot 5$

9. Evaluate the expression when $x = {}^{-}2$ and $y = 4$.

$$(y^2 + 2) \div x$$

A $^{-}9$

B $^{-}8$

C $1\frac{1}{2}$

D 9

10. What value of *z* makes this equation true?

$$z - {}^{-}4 = 12$$

A 48

B 16

C 8

D $^{-}8$

11. Which equation has a solution of $^{-}4$?

A $^{+}7 + d \cdot {}^{-}6 = {}^{+}31$

B $d + {}^{+}20 = {}^{+}11$

C $d + {}^{+}20 = {}^{+}24$

D $^{-}5d \div {}^{-}10 = {}^{+}2$

Read the questions. Use the strategies to choose the answer choice that makes the most sense.

STRATEGIES

1. **Solve the equation.**

$$^-154 = ^-7p$$

    A $^+1078$ **C** $^+22$

    B $^+147$ **D** $^-22$

• Divide both sides of the equation by $^-7$ to isolate the variable p.

$$p = ^-154 \div ^-7$$
$$p = ^+22$$

Think
If the dividend and divisor have the same sign, the quotient is positive.

Answer choice C is correct.

2. **This chart below shows the change in temperature from morning to evening during the week. What was the change in temperature on Tuesday?**

Day	Temperature	
	Morning	**Evening**
Monday	$^-4°C$	$3°C$
Tuesday	$^-6°C$	$^-4°C$
Wednesday	$0°C$	$^-2°C$

    A $^-10°C$ **C** $2°C$

    B $^-2°C$ **D** $10°C$

• Subtract the smaller number from the larger number to find a difference or change.

$$^-6 < ^-4$$

• Rewrite integer subtraction as integer addition, and then use a number line to solve.

$$^-4 - ^-6 =$$
$$^-4 + ^+6 = ^+2$$
$$\downarrow$$
   subtrahend

Remember: Change the sign of the subtrahend when you rewrite integer subtraction as integer addition.

• You can use a number line to help.

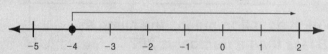

Answer choice C is correct.

3. **An outside thermometer reads $^-5°C$. About what temperature is that in degrees Fahrenheit?**

    A about $40°F$ C about $20°F$

    B about $41°F$ D about $^-20°F$

Think
You can use a formula to estimate degrees Celsius to degrees Fahrenheit.

• Use this formula to estimate -5°C to °F.

$$°F \approx (2°C + 30)$$
$$\approx (2 \cdot ^-5 + 30)$$
$$\approx ^-10 + 30$$
$$\approx 20$$

Think
Replace C with $^-5$.

Answer choice C is correct.

Circle the letter of the correct answer choice.

---

4. Evaluate the expression.

$$9 - (^-1 - 3) \times 3^2$$

   A 117   **C** 33

   B 45   **D** 27

---

5. Evaluate the expression when $j = ^-3$.

$$^-2[3 + (14 - j^2)^2]$$

   A $^-56$ **C** $^-16$

   B $^-28$ **D** 56

---

6. Luis collected 24 baseball cards this year. That is three times more than the number of cards he collected last year. How many cards did he collect last year?

   A 72   **C** 21

   B 27   **D** 8

---

7. Which equation means the same as *$^-8$ less than a number is 20*?

   A $b - 8 = 20$

   B $^-8 - b = 20$

   C $b - ^-8 = 20$

   D $20 - ^-8 = b$

---

8. Bill started in the middle of a ladder. He climbed up 10 feet, then slid down 4 feet. What was his overall change in position?

   A $^+14$ feet   **C** $^-6$ feet

   B $^+6$ feet   **D** $^-14$ feet

---

9. The average low temperature in a northern town last February was $^-2°C$. Use the formula below to estimate the temperature in °F.

$$°F \approx (2°C + 30)$$

   A about $^-34°F$ **C** about $^+34°F$

   B about $^+26°F$ **D** about $^-26°F$

---

10. How much did the temperature change from Wednesday to Thursday?

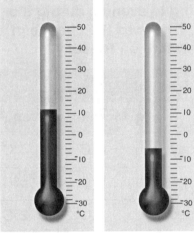

Wednesday   Thursday

   A $^-18°C$ **C** $^-6°C$

   B $^-8°C$ **D** $^+14°C$

---

11. Find the value of x in the following equation.

$$6 - x = ^-1$$

   A 7   **C** $^-5$

   B 5   **D** $^-7$

Read the questions. Use the strategies to choose
the answer choice that makes the most sense.

STRATEGIES

---

1. Which number is divisible by 2 and 3?

A 4714

B 5788

C 9256

D 8496

• Look at the underlined digit(s). Use them to help you understand the divisibility rules that follow.

4**4**: Even. Divisible by 2.
4**5** or 4**0**: Ends in 5 or 0; Divisible by 5.
5**0**: Ends in 0: Divisible by 10.
3**16**: Last 2 digits divisible by 4: Divisible by 4.
3591: Sum of all digits divisible by 3: Divisible by 3.
5058: Sum all digits divisible by 9: Divisible by 9.

• All answer choices end with an even number. They are all divisible by 2.

• Find the answer choice that also has a sum that is divisible by 3.

Answer choice D is correct.

---

2. What is the prime factorization of the number 54?

A $2^2 \times 3^3$

B $3^2 \times 2^3$

C 2×3^3

D $3^2 \times 3^3$

Remember: A **prime number** has two factors: 1 and itself. **Composite numbers** have more than two factors.

You can make a factor tree to find the prime factorization of the number 54.

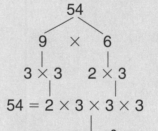

$$54 = 2 \times 3 \times 3 \times 3$$

$$54 = \mathbf{2 \times 3^3} \longleftarrow 3 \times 3 \times 3 = 3^3$$

• Start with the composite number
• Choose *any* 2 factors.
• Continue factoring until all the branches show *prime numbers*
• Arrange the prime factors in order from least to greatest.

Answer choice C is correct.

---

3. Which fractions are equivalent to the fraction $\frac{16}{20}$?

A $\frac{32}{40}, \frac{5}{6}$ **C** $\frac{5}{12}, \frac{32}{36}$

B $\frac{4}{5}, \frac{6}{8}$ **D** $\frac{32}{40}, \frac{4}{5}$

• Multiply or divide both terms of a fraction by the same nonzero number to find equivalent fractions.

• Multiply. $\frac{16}{20} = \frac{16 \times 2}{20 \times 2} = \frac{32}{40}$ $\frac{16}{20} = \frac{32}{40}$ **equivalent**

• Divide. $\frac{16}{20} = \frac{16 \div 4}{20 \div 4} = \frac{4}{5}$ $\frac{16}{20} = \frac{4}{5}$ **equivalent**

Answer choice D is correct.

Name _____

Circle the letter of the correct answer choice.

---

4. What is the prime factorization of 225?

  A $3^2 \times 5^3$

  B $3^2 \times 5^2$

  C 3×5^3

  D $3^2 \times 3^3$

---

5. Which fractions are equivalent to the fraction $\frac{7}{9}$?

  A $\frac{14}{18}, \frac{12}{15}$

  B $\frac{12}{16}, \frac{21}{27}$

  C $\frac{14}{18}, \frac{21}{27}$

  D $\frac{28}{35}, \frac{42}{45}$

---

6. Which of the following numbers are all prime numbers?

  A 5, 23, 11, 79

  B 5, 17, 21, 59

  C 1, 4, 8, 18

  D 2, 3, 17, 27

---

7. Which of the following numbers are all composite numbers?

  A 6, 15, 17, 29   **C** 4, 8, 12, 31

  B 6, 7, 9, 14   **D** 6, 15, 24, 32

---

8. Which number is divisible by 3 and 4?

  A 7320

  B 4682

  C 3491

  D 9154

---

9. The prime factorization $3^2 \times 31$ is the prime factorization for which number?

  A 56   **C** 279

  B 78   **D** 1665

---

10. Which fractions are equivalent to $\frac{6}{8}$?

  A $\frac{4}{12}, \frac{3}{4}, \frac{9}{12}$

  B $\frac{3}{4}, \frac{12}{16}, \frac{24}{40}$

  C $\frac{12}{16}, \frac{16}{32}, \frac{30}{48}$

  D $\frac{3}{4}, \frac{18}{24}, \frac{36}{48}$

---

11. Solve for the missing term. $\frac{n}{15} = \frac{36}{45}$

  A $n = 12$

  B $n = 16$

  C $n = 18$

  D $n = 24$

---

12. Solve for y to complete the prime factorization.

$$90 = y \times 3^2 \times 5$$

  A $y = 1$

  B $y = 2^3$

  C $y = 2^2$

  D $y = 2$

Read the questions. Use the strategies to choose the answer choice that makes the most sense.

STRATEGIES

1. What is the least common multiple (LCM) of 3, 4, and 18?

   A 24

   B 36

   C 48

   D 54

Remember: The **least common multiple (LCM)** of two or more numbers is the least number, except 0, that is a common multiple for both (or all) of the numbers.

• List multiples of each number. Extend the list until you find a common multiple of the numbers.

   3: 3, 6, 9, 12, 15, 18, 21, 24, 27, 30, 33, **36**. . .

   4: 4, 8, 12, 16, 20, 24, 28, 32, **36**, 40, 44, 48. . .

   18: 18, **36**. . .

The LCM of 3, 4, and 18 is 36.

Answer choice B is correct.

---

2. Which shows the numbers $4\frac{1}{3}, \frac{24}{5}, 4\frac{3}{15}$ in order from greatest to least?

   A $4\frac{1}{3}, \frac{24}{5}, 4\frac{3}{15}$ C $\frac{24}{5}, 4\frac{1}{3}, 4\frac{3}{15}$

   B $\frac{24}{5}, 4\frac{3}{15}, 4\frac{1}{3}$ D $4\frac{3}{15}, \frac{24}{5}, 4\frac{1}{3}$

• Write the improper fraction as a mixed number.

$$\frac{24}{5} = 4\frac{4}{5}$$

• Compare the whole numbers.

$$4 = 4 = 4$$

• Rename each fraction using the LCD.

$$4\frac{5}{15}, 4\frac{3}{15}, 4\frac{12}{15}$$

Remember: The **LCD** of two or more fractions is the **LCM** of the denominators. **LCD = 15**

• Compare the numerators.

$$\frac{12}{15} > \frac{5}{15} > \frac{3}{15}$$

• Write the numbers from greatest to least.

$$\frac{24}{5}, 4\frac{1}{3}, 4\frac{3}{15}$$

Answer choice C is correct.

---

3. What is 0.24 expressed as a fraction in simplest form?

   A $\frac{24}{100}$ C $\frac{6}{25}$

   B $\frac{4}{5}$ D $\frac{9}{10}$

• Read the given decimal.

   0.24 → twenty-four hundredths

• Determine the denominator of the fraction. The denominator of the fraction is 100.

• Write an equivalent fraction.

   twenty-four hundredths → $\frac{24}{100}$

• Simplify if necessary. $\frac{24}{100} = \frac{6}{25}$

Answer choice C is correct. $0.24 = \frac{6}{25}$

Name _____

Circle the letter of the correct answer choice.

4. **What is the least common multiple (LCM) of 4, 6, and 9?**

   A 12

   B 16

   C 24

   D 36

5. **Which shows the numbers $7\frac{5}{12}, 7\frac{1}{2}, 7\frac{3}{8}$ in order from least to greatest?**

   A $7\frac{5}{12}, 7\frac{1}{2}, 7\frac{3}{8}$

   B $7\frac{1}{2}, 7\frac{5}{12}, 7\frac{3}{8}$

   C $7\frac{3}{8}, 7\frac{5}{12}, 7\frac{1}{2}$

   D $7\frac{3}{8}, 7\frac{1}{2}, 7\frac{5}{12}$

6. **Recipe A calls for $1\frac{2}{3}$ c flour, recipe B calls for $1\frac{2}{4}$ c flour, recipe C calls for $1\frac{1}{2}$ c flour, and recipe D calls for $1\frac{3}{5}$ c flour. Which recipe calls for the most flour?**

   A Recipe A

   B Recipe B

   C Recipe C

   D Recipe D

7. **Eighty-four is the least common multiple (LCM) of which set of numbers?**

   A 3, 4, and 6

   B 3, 4, and 7

   C 3, 4, and 18

   D 5, 8, and 20

8. **Which is equivalent to $9\frac{17}{100}$?**

   A 0.917

   B 0.00917

   C 9.17

   D 917

9. **If Karen has four eighths of a dollar how much money does she have?**

   A $0.35

   B $0.25

   C $0.48

   D $0.50

10. **What is 0.125 expressed as a fraction in simplest form?**

   A $\frac{1}{8}$

   B $\frac{125}{100}$

   C $\frac{125}{1000}$

   D $\frac{3}{8}$

Read the questions. Use the strategies to choose the answer choice that makes the most sense.

---

1. Which shows $\frac{5}{9}$ as a repeating decimal?

A $0.\overline{5}$

B 0.50

C 0.05

D 0.005

Remember: A ***terminating decimal*** has a remainder of 0. A ***repeating decimal*** has one or more digits that repeat over and over again.

$\frac{5}{9}$ means
$$9\overline{)5.00} \quad \begin{array}{c} .55 \\ \end{array}$$
-45 ← Add zeros as needed.
$\overline{50}$

$5 \div 9$.

Think

The next number in the quotient will always be 5 and the remainder will always be 5.

$\frac{5}{9} = 0.\overline{5}$ ← The bar shows digits that repeat.

Answer choice A is correct.

---

2. Identify the rational number at point P on the number line.

A $^+1.75$

C $^+1\frac{1}{4}$

B 2

D $^+\frac{1}{0}$

Remember: **Rational numbers** are integers, whole numbers, and fractions whose denominators are not zero.

• Analyze answer choices.
  ▸ A fraction with a denominator of zero is **not** a rational number. **D** is not a possible answer.
  ▸ Point P is **not** on the mark above $^+2$ or 2. **B** is **not** a possible answer.
  ▸ Compare **C**, $^+1\frac{1}{4}$ and **A**, $^+1.75$. Write $^+1\frac{1}{4}$ as $^+1.25$.

Think

Point P is closer to $^+2$ than to $^+1$.
$^+1.75$ is closer to $^+2$ than $^+1\frac{1}{4}$.

Answer choice A is correct.

---

3. Which answer choice shows the rational numbers in order from *least* to *greatest*?

A $^-3\frac{1}{2}, ^-3.25, ^-3\frac{3}{4}$

B $^-3\frac{3}{4}, ^-3\frac{1}{2}, ^-3.25$

C $^-3.25, ^-3\frac{3}{4}, ^-3\frac{1}{2}$

D $^-3.25, ^-3\frac{1}{2}, ^-3\frac{3}{4}$

• Write the numbers as either decimals or fractions.

Fractions: $^-3\frac{1}{4}, ^-3\frac{1}{2}, ^-3\frac{3}{4}$

Decimals: $^-3.25, ^-3.5, ^-3.75$

• Use a number line to compare.

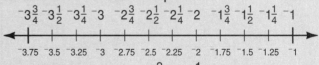

From least to greatest: $^-3\frac{3}{4}, ^-3\frac{1}{2}, ^-3.25$

Answer choice B is correct.

Circle the letter of the correct answer choice.

---

4. Rename the fraction $\frac{5}{8}$ as a terminating or repeating decimal.

   A 0.625

   B $0.6\overline{6}$

   C 0.0625

   D 0.06255

5. Jim plays baseball for his high school team. So far, he has been at bat 33 times and has gotten 13 hits. When rounded to the nearest thousandth, what is Jim's batting average?

   A 0.39

   B 0.3939

   C 0.393

   D 0.394

6. Which of the following is *not* a rational number?

   A 7

   B $-\frac{5}{9}$

   C $\frac{6}{0}$

   D 1.7

7. This table records a runner's results on plays during a football game. On which play did he have the greatest loss?

Play	Yards
1	$+5\frac{1}{4}$
2	-2
3	3.5
4	$-1\frac{1}{2}$

   A Play 1

   B Play 2

   C Play 3

   D Play 4

8. Which answer choice shows the numbers in order from *greatest* to *least*?

   A $-\frac{3}{4}, -0.5, \frac{1}{5}, 0$

   B $\frac{1}{5}, 0, -0.5, -\frac{3}{4}$

   C $-\frac{3}{4}, -0.5, 0, \frac{1}{5}$

   D $0, \frac{1}{5}, -0.5, -\frac{3}{4}$

9. Which will give a terminating decimal as a quotient?

   A $1 \div 9$

   B $1 \div 6$

   C $1 \div 4$

   D $1 \div 11$

Read the questions. Use the strategies to choose the answer choice that makes the most sense.

STRATEGIES

1. Estimate the sum.

$$\frac{5}{8} + \frac{3}{4}$$

A 1   **C** $1\frac{1}{2}$

B $\frac{1}{2}$ **D** 2

You can use a number line to round fractions to 0, $\frac{1}{2}$, or 1 to estimate sums or differences.

Think
$\frac{3}{4}$ is close to 1.
$\frac{5}{8}$ is close to $\frac{1}{2}$.

• Add the rounded numbers: $\frac{1}{2} + 1 = 1\frac{1}{2}$

Answer choice C is correct.

2. Find the sum.

$$2\frac{7}{8} + 2\frac{1}{6} + \frac{1}{4}$$

A $5\frac{7}{24}$

B $4\frac{12}{24}$

C 4

D $5\frac{5}{12}$

• Estimate by rounding to the nearest whole number.

$$2\frac{7}{8} + 2\frac{1}{6} + \frac{1}{4}$$

Add the rounded numbers: $3 + 2 + 0 = 5$

• Use multiples to find the least common denominator (LCD) of the fractions.

Multiples of 8: 8, 16, **24**, 32 . . .

Multiples of 6: 6, 12, 18, **24**, 30 . . .

Multiples of 4: 4, 8, 12, 16, 20, **24**, 28 . . .

The LCD is 24.

• Rename each fraction as an equivalent fraction with the LCD as the denominator.

$$2\frac{7}{8} = \frac{7 \times 3}{8 \times 3} = 2\frac{21}{24}; 2\frac{1}{6} = \frac{1 \times 4}{6 \times 4} = 2\frac{4}{24}; \text{ and}$$

$$\frac{1}{4} = \frac{1 \times 6}{4 \times 6} = \frac{6}{24}$$

• Add. Express the sum in simplest form.

$$2\frac{21}{24} + 2\frac{4}{24} + \frac{6}{24} = 4\frac{31}{24} = 4 + \frac{7}{24} = 5\frac{7}{24}$$

$5\frac{7}{24}$ is close to the estimate of 5.

Answer choice A is correct.

Circle the letter of the correct answer choice.

3. **Estimate the sum.**

$$\frac{1}{10} + \frac{8}{15} + \frac{4}{9}$$

A about 1

B about 2

C about 3

D about 4

4. **Find the sum.**

$$\frac{7}{9} + \frac{1}{2} + \frac{1}{6}$$

A $\frac{9}{17}$ C $1\frac{4}{17}$

B $\frac{6}{45}$ D $1\frac{4}{9}$

5. **Find the difference in simplest form.**

$$5\frac{1}{2} - 4\frac{3}{10}$$

A $9\frac{4}{5}$ C $1\frac{1}{5}$

B $1\frac{2}{8}$ D $1\frac{2}{5}$

6. **Estimate the sum.**

$$3 + 9\frac{3}{4} + 2\frac{1}{8}$$

A about 14   C about 16

B about 15   D about $20\frac{5}{8}$

7. **The least common denominator to find the sum of $1\frac{3}{8} + \frac{5}{12}$ is 24. What is another common denominator that could be used to find the sum of the fractions?**

A 12

B 18

C 36

D 48

8. **A recipe calls for $4\frac{1}{2}$ c of water and $1\frac{1}{3}$ c of lemon juice. What is the total amount of liquid in the recipe?**

A $5\frac{5}{6}$

B $5\frac{2}{5}$

C $5\frac{3}{4}$

D $6\frac{3}{4}$

9. **Estimate the difference.**

$$10\frac{1}{2} - 8\frac{3}{5}$$

A about 2

B about $1\frac{1}{5}$

C about 1

D about $2\frac{1}{2}$

Read the questions. Use the strategies to choose
the answer choice that makes the most sense.

STRATEGIES

1. Subtract: $\frac{5}{6} - \frac{1}{4}$

A 0

B $\frac{7}{12}$

C $\frac{2}{3}$

D 2

- Use multiples to find the LCD of the fractions.

  Multiples of 6: 6, **12**, 18, 24 . . .   The LCD is 12.

  Multiples of 4: 4, 8, **12**, 16 . . .

- Rename. $\frac{5}{6} = \frac{5 \times 2}{6 \times 2} = \frac{10}{12}$ $\frac{1}{4} = \frac{1 \times 3}{4 \times 3} = \frac{3}{12}$

- Subtract. $\frac{10}{12} - \frac{3}{12} = \frac{7}{12}$ Simplify if necessary.

Answer choice B is correct.

2. Makel needs $5\frac{1}{4}$ **yards of rope to tie
up his boat. He has** $3\frac{3}{4}$ **yards. How
many more yards of rope does he
need?**

A $1\frac{3}{4}$ yd   C $\frac{3}{4}$ yd

B $1\frac{1}{2}$ yd   D $2\frac{1}{2}$ yd

Subtract to find how many more yd (y) are needed.

- First estimate:

$$5\frac{1}{4} - 3\frac{3}{4} = y \longrightarrow 5 - 4 = 1$$

Think
$\frac{3}{4} > \frac{1}{4}$. Rename then subtract.

$$5\frac{1}{4} = 4 + 1 + \frac{1}{4} = 4 + \frac{4}{4} + \frac{1}{4} = 4\frac{5}{4}$$

Remember: If denominators
are different, you will need to
use the LCD to rename as
equivalent fractions before
you subtract.

$$\begin{array}{r} 4\frac{5}{4} \\ - 3\frac{3}{4} \\ \hline 1\frac{2}{4} \end{array} \longrightarrow 1\frac{1}{2}$$

simplest form

Answer choice B, $1\frac{1}{2}$, **is correct.**

3. What is the value of m?

$$m + \frac{1}{3} = \frac{1}{2}$$

A 1   C $\frac{2}{6}$

B $\frac{1}{2}$ D $\frac{1}{6}$

- You can use a related addition or subtraction
  sentence to find the missing value in the equation.

$m + \frac{1}{3} = \frac{1}{2}$ related subtraction sentence $m = \frac{1}{2} - \frac{1}{3}$

- Rename each fraction with the LCD of 2 and 3.

$$m = \frac{3}{6} - \frac{2}{6} = \frac{1}{6} \qquad m = \frac{1}{6}$$

Answer choice D is correct.

Circle the letter of the correct answer choice.

4. Subtract: $\frac{7}{8} - \frac{1}{2}$

 A $\frac{3}{8}$ C $\frac{3}{4}$

 B $\frac{5}{8}$ D $\frac{3}{2}$

7. Subtract: $9\frac{1}{12} - 4\frac{5}{8}$

 A $4\frac{10}{24}$ C $5\frac{1}{4}$

 B $4\frac{11}{24}$ D $5\frac{11}{24}$

5. This table shows the parts of an hour Tommy spent on his chores. How much more time did he spend cleaning his room than taking out the trash?

Chore	Time (fraction of an hour)
Washing dishes	$\frac{1}{2}$
Taking out trash	$\frac{1}{6}$
Cleaning room	$\frac{3}{4}$

 A $\frac{1}{3}$ C $\frac{5}{6}$

 B $\frac{1}{2}$ D $\frac{7}{12}$

8. Mary will run a total of 8 miles in a charity race. She has run $3\frac{1}{4}$ miles so far. How many more miles does she have to go?

 A $4\frac{1}{4}$ C $5\frac{1}{4}$

 B $4\frac{3}{4}$ D $5\frac{3}{4}$

9. Find the missing fraction.

$$\frac{1}{4} = n - \frac{1}{16}$$

 A $\frac{2}{20}$ C $\frac{5}{16}$

 B $\frac{7}{16}$ D $\frac{9}{16}$

6. Find the value of d.

$$d + \frac{3}{10} = \frac{4}{5}$$

 A $\frac{1}{10}$

 B $\frac{1}{2}$

 C $\frac{7}{10}$

 D $\frac{11}{10}$

10. A dog has three puppies. One puppy weighed $2\frac{1}{8}$ lb, one weighed $2\frac{3}{4}$ lb, and the third weighed 3 lb. What is the difference in weights of the puppy that weighed the most and the puppy that weighed the least?

 A $\frac{7}{8}$ lb   C $\frac{1}{2}$ lb

 B $\frac{1}{4}$ lb   D 1

Read the questions. Use the strategies to choose the answer choice that makes the most sense.

1. Evaluate the expression

$$b + 3\frac{1}{2} + c + 2\frac{3}{5}, \text{ when } b = 3\frac{4}{5}$$

and $c = 1\frac{1}{2}$.

A $11\frac{2}{5}$

B $13\frac{1}{2}$

C $11\frac{1}{5}$

D $16\frac{2}{5}$

Follow these steps to evaluate the expression:

• Replace b with $3\frac{4}{5}$ and c with $1\frac{1}{2}$.

$$\underset{\underset{b}{\uparrow}}{3\frac{4}{5}} + 3\frac{1}{2} + \underset{\underset{c}{\uparrow}}{1\frac{1}{2}} + 2\frac{3}{5}$$

• Use the Commutative and Associative Properties.

> Remember: Commutative means "order."
> Associative means "grouping."

$$\left(3\frac{4}{5} + 2\frac{3}{5}\right) + \left(3\frac{1}{2} + 1\frac{1}{2}\right) \quad \substack{\text{fractions have like} \\ \leftarrow \text{denominators}}$$

• Simplify using the order of operations.

$$\left(3\frac{4}{5} + 2\frac{3}{5}\right) + \left(3\frac{1}{2} + 1\frac{1}{2}\right)$$

$$5\frac{7}{5} \rightarrow 6\frac{2}{5} + 4\frac{2}{2} \rightarrow 5$$

$$6\frac{2}{5} + 5 = 11\frac{2}{5}$$

Answer choice A is correct.

2. Solve the equation. Write in simplest form.

$$5\frac{7}{8} - d = \frac{3}{8}$$

A $d = 5\frac{10}{8}$

B $d = 6\frac{2}{8}$

C $d = 5\frac{4}{8}$

D $d = 5\frac{1}{2}$

---**Think**---
You can solve equations with fractions the same way as you solve equations with whole numbers.

• Add the variable, d, to both sides as you would a whole number or fraction.

$$5\frac{7}{8} - d + d = \frac{3}{8} + d \longrightarrow 5\frac{7}{8} = \frac{3}{8} + d$$

• Subtract $\frac{3}{8}$ from both sides to isolate the variable.

$$5\frac{7}{8} - \frac{3}{8} = \frac{3}{8} + d - \frac{3}{8} \longrightarrow 5\frac{7}{8} - \frac{3}{8} = d + \frac{3}{8} - \frac{3}{8}$$

$$5\frac{7}{8} - \frac{3}{8} = d + \frac{3}{8} - \frac{3}{8} \qquad 5\frac{4}{8} = d \text{ or } d = 5\frac{4}{8}$$

• Write in simplest form if necessary. $5\frac{1}{2}$

Answer choice D is correct.

Circle the letter of the correct answer choice.

3. Evaluate the expression $m - 4\frac{1}{2} + s$

   when $m = 8\frac{4}{5}$ and $s = 3\frac{1}{5}$.

   A $5\frac{4}{5}$ C $7\frac{3}{4}$

   B $7\frac{1}{2}$ D $8\frac{1}{2}$

4. Solve: $h + 9\frac{3}{4} = 15\frac{1}{2}$

   A $h = 4\frac{1}{2}$ C $h = 5\frac{3}{4}$

   B $h = 4\frac{3}{4}$ D $h = 6\frac{3}{4}$

5. Scott has some green squash and $2\frac{1}{2}$ pounds of yellow squash. He has a total of $4\frac{1}{4}$ pounds of squash. Which equation could be used to find how many pounds of green squash Scott has?

   A $n + 2\frac{1}{2} = 4\frac{1}{4}$

   B $n + 4\frac{1}{4} = 2\frac{1}{2}$

   C $n = 2\frac{1}{2} + 4\frac{1}{4}$

   D $n - 4\frac{1}{4} = 2\frac{1}{2}$

6. Kristin does not know her score on her first vault routing. She scores $7\frac{3}{4}$ on her second vault. If her total score is $14\frac{1}{4}$, what was her first score? Which equation could be used to solve this problem?

   A $v + 7\frac{3}{4} = 14\frac{1}{4}$

   B $7\frac{3}{4} + 14\frac{1}{4} = v$

   C $7\frac{3}{4} - v = 14\frac{1}{4}$

   D $v - 7\frac{3}{4} = 14\frac{3}{4}$

7. Evaluate:

   $p + 1 + 8\frac{1}{6} + 2\frac{3}{4}$, when $p = 2\frac{5}{6}$

   A $11\frac{11}{12}$ C $12\frac{2}{5}$

   B $14\frac{1}{4}$ D $14\frac{3}{4}$

8. Solve the equation.

   $$f + 3\frac{4}{5} = 11\frac{1}{4}$$

   A $f = 7\frac{9}{20}$ C $f = 7\frac{11}{20}$

   B $f = 7\frac{4}{5}$ D $f = 7\frac{5}{9}$

Read the problem. Use the Problem-Solving Guide
below to help you think about the answer choices.

An air balloon is flying 144 m above sea level while a diver swims
directly underneath at 45 m below sea level. What is the expanse
between them?

A ⁻45 m

B 99 m

C 189 m

D ⁻189 m

PROBLEM-SOLVING GUIDE

① Understand the Question

- The question is asking you to find the
answer choice that shows the expanse
between an air balloon above sea level and
a diver below sea level.

- Each answer choice shows a length
measure in meters.

② Understand Word Meanings

- The *expanse* is the distance or stretch of
area between the air balloon and the diver.

- You can reveal the meaning of the word by
noting the measurement being used in the
problem. A meter (m) represents metric
length or *distance*.

③ Understand How to Solve

- Reread the question if you need to.

- Write the distance of the air balloon flying *above sea level*. ⁺144 m

- Write the distance of the diver swimming *below sea level*. ⁻45 m

- Choose the operation you will use to solve and write the equation: addition
total expanse = ⁺144 m + | ⁻45 m |

- Then solve.

    ⁺144 m + ⁺45 m = ⁺189 m

Think
The absolute value of an integer is its *distance*
from zero on a number line. Since the sea level
represents zero and you are adding the two
distances *above* and *below*, you must take the
absolute value of ⁻45 m.

④ Circle the Letter of the Correct Answer Choice.

Answer choice C is correct.
The expanse between the air balloon and the diver is 189 m.

Name _____

Circle the letter of the correct answer choice.

This table shows the type of pizza pies sold at Polly's Pizza Parlor yesterday. What is the amassed amount of cheese and veggie pizza sold?

Pizza Pies	Amount Sold
Cheese	$4\frac{2}{3}$
Meatball	$1\frac{1}{2}$
Sausage	$2\frac{1}{4}$
Veggie	$3\frac{3}{4}$

A $7\frac{5}{12}$ **C** $7\frac{5}{7}$

B $7\frac{1}{2}$ **D** $8\frac{5}{12}$

Complete each sentence.

1 Understand the Question

- Polly sold _____ cheese pizzas and _____ veggie pizzas.

- The question is asking you to find the answer choice that tells _____ .

- The answer choices are each _____ .

2 Understand Word Meanings: amassed

- The *prefix a-* means "to" and *massa-* from Latin means "lump together."

- Write what you think **amassed** means. _____

3 Understand How to Solve

- Reread the _____ if you need to.

- First, choose the correct operation: _____

- Then, set up the problem and solve:

$$\begin{array}{cc} 4 & \frac{2}{3} \\ +3 & \frac{3}{4} \\ \hline \end{array} \rightarrow \begin{array}{cc} 4 & \frac{8}{12} \\ +3 & \frac{9}{12} \\ \hline 7 & \frac{17}{12} = 8\frac{5}{12} \end{array}$$

> Remember: To add find the least common denominator.

4 Circle the Letter of the Correct Answer Choice.

Answer choice D is correct. Polly's Pizza Parlor sold a total of _____ cheese and veggie pizzas.

Name _____

Circle the letter of the correct answer choice.

---

1. This table shows the average temperatures for a week in Juneau, Alaska. On which day was the temperature the lowest?

Average Temperatures in Juneau, Alaska						
Mon.	Tues.	Wed.	Thurs.	Fri.	Sat.	Sun.
⁻5°F	⁻3°F	2°F	⁻7°F	0°F	⁻1°F	⁻2°F

   A Monday

   B Wednesday

   C Thursday

   D Friday

---

2. Helen started with $47.00 in her savings account. Then she spent $16 and deposited $11. Finally, she earned $1.59 in interest. Which expression shows her current balance?

   A $47 + {}^-16 + 11 + 1.59$

   B $47 - ({}^-16) + 11 + 1.59$

   C $47 + 16 + 11 + 1.59$

   D ${}^-47 + ({}^-16) + 11 + 1.59$

---

3. Gordon owes Lance $93.00. He will pay the money back in equal amounts over 6 months. How can he figure out how his bank account will change each month?

   A multiply ⁻93 times 6

   B divide ⁻93 by 6

   C multiply 93 times ⁻6

   D divide ⁻93 by ⁻6

---

4. Amanda is thinking of a number that is 14 less than three times negative six. What is the number?

   A ⁻32   **C** 4

   B ⁻4   **D** 32

---

5. The July temperature at a science stations in Antarctica is ⁻47°F and 84°F in Ecuador. How many degrees warmer is it in Ecuador?

   A ⁻37°F

   B 37°F

   C 121°F

   D 131°F

---

6. The formula for converting degrees Celsius to degrees Fahrenheit is
°F ≈ 2°C + 30.

   If the average February temperature in Boston is 3°C, what is the temperature in degrees Fahrenheit?

   A 32°F   **C** 6°F

   B 28°F   **D** 36°F

---

7. Rich bought x shares of stock at $8.00 per share. Then the stock's value dropped to $5.00 per share. Which expression shows his total loss?

   A ⁻3x **C** 5x

   B ⁻5x **D** 13x

Problem Solving Workshop 2

8. Mrs. McFarlane is buying stickers for her 3 children. Which number of stickers can she buy so that they each get the same number with none left over?

   A 79   **C** 81

   B 80   **D** 82

---

9. Kelly recognized a pattern in the numbers. What pattern did she see?

   2, 3, 5, 7, 11, 13, 17

   A The numbers are odd.

   B The pattern is +1, +2, +3, +4 and so on.

   C The numbers are prime.

   D The numbers are composite.

---

10. The prime factors of a certain number are 2, 3, and 3. What is the number?

    A 6   **C** 18

    B 8   **D** 233

---

11. Randy is reducing $\frac{27}{72}$ to simplest form. Which number should he use as the greatest common factor?

    A 3   **C** 9

    B 6   **D** 27

---

12. Lauren sold $14\frac{3}{8}$ pitchers of lemonade at a lemonade stand. If each serving was $\frac{1}{8}$ pitcher, how many servings did she sell?

    A 50   **C** 115

    B 112   **D** 143

---

13. Which answer choice does *not* represent the shaded part of the figure?

    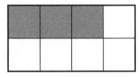

    A $\frac{10}{16}$ **C** $\frac{3}{8}$

    B $\frac{9}{24}$ **D** $\frac{6}{16}$

---

14. Bonnie made 147 bookmarks to sell at the school fair. Each bookmark used $\frac{1}{5}$ sheet of paper. How many whole sheets of paper did she use?

    A 29   **C** 152

    B 30   **D** 735

Name _____

Circle the letter of the correct answer choice.

---

15. The length of one side of a square, *s*, equals one-fourth of the perimeter, *P*. Which equation shows this relationship?

    A $s = 4P$ **C** $s = 0.14P$

    B $s = 0.4P$ **D** $s = 0.25P$

---

16. If these boys lined up from tallest to shortest, what would be the correct order? [Hint: 12 in. = 1 ft]

Leo	Alexander	Oliver	Joe
$60\frac{1}{8}$ inches	4 feet 11 inches	5 feet $\frac{13}{16}$ inches	$60\frac{7}{8}$ inches

    A Joe, Oliver, Leo, Alexander

    B Joe, Alexander, Oliver, Leo

    C Joe, Leo, Oliver, Alexander

    D Alexander, Leo, Oliver, Joe

---

17. Which inequality shows the numbers in correct order?

    A $^-0.25 < \frac{1}{9} < 4.8$

    B $\frac{2}{3} < .897 < {}^-0.6$

    C $^-0.59 < \frac{^-9}{10} < 0.617$

    D $^-4\frac{3}{7} < 1.88 < 1\frac{3}{5}$

---

18. The three fastest runners in the 100-meter dash completed a race with finishing times within $\frac{1}{8}$-second of each other. Which answer choice could show their finishing times?

    A 11.125, 11.225, 11.325

    B 10.375, 10.575, 10.700

    C 12.675, 12.800, 12.950

    D 12.850, 12.975, 13.100

---

19. It takes 44 hours for the Duluth Car Company to produce 3 cars from start to finish. To the nearest tenth of an hour, how long does it take to build one car?

    A 14.6 hours   **C** 41 hours

    B 14.7 hours   **D** 47 hours

---

20. Which fraction can be represented as repeating decimal?

    A $\frac{1}{8}$ **C** $\frac{4}{9}$

    B $\frac{3}{8}$ **D** $\frac{7}{10}$

---

21. This table shows rainfall in the desert over 4 months. In which month was there the least rainfall?

Desert Rainfall, November–February			
November	**December**	**January**	**February**
$\frac{1}{16}''$	$\frac{3}{32}''$	$\frac{1}{8}''$	$\frac{3}{16}''$

    A November   **C** January

    B December   **D** February

Problem Solving Workshop 2

22. Joy, May, and Ella are making a quilt together. Joy has finished $\frac{1}{3}$ of the quilt and May has finished $\frac{3}{8}$. How much of the quilt is left for Ella to finish?

A $\frac{1}{24}$ C $\frac{8}{24}$

B $\frac{7}{24}$ D $\frac{17}{24}$

23. Brian is figuring out the total number of hours that he worked last week. What is the best estimate?

Hours Worked				
Mon.	Tues.	Wed.	Thurs.	Fri.
$2\frac{1}{4}$	$3\frac{7}{8}$	$5\frac{1}{2}$	$2\frac{3}{4}$	$3\frac{1}{2}$

A about 15   C about 19

B about 16   D about 20

24. When Tyler went to bed on Wednesday, he had read $\frac{3}{4}$ of his book. At the beginning of the day, he had read only $\frac{3}{5}$ of the book. What fraction of the book did he read on Wednesday?

A $\frac{1}{3}$ C $\frac{15}{20}$

B $\frac{3}{20}$ D $1\frac{7}{20}$

25. Brent made 7 cakes for the school bake sale. If he sold $2\frac{2}{3}$ cakes and gave away $2\frac{1}{2}$ cakes, how much cake was left over after the sale?

A $\frac{1}{6}$ C $2\frac{5}{6}$

B $1\frac{5}{6}$ D $5\frac{1}{6}$

26. Lexie's goal is to knit $\frac{3}{5}$ of a sweater by Friday. She has already knitted $\frac{1}{3}$ of the sweater. Which equation will tell her how much is left to knit?

A $x - \frac{3}{5} = \frac{1}{3}$ C $\frac{1}{3} - x = \frac{3}{5}$

B $x = \frac{1}{3} - \frac{3}{5}$ D $\frac{1}{3} + x = \frac{3}{5}$

27. Together, John, Max, and Rena ate $1\frac{1}{2}$ pizza's. How much pizza did Rena eat?
[Hint: Shaded portion = pizza eaten]

John's Pizza   Max's Pizza   Rena's Pizza

A $\frac{5}{8}$ C $\frac{8}{8}$

B $\frac{7}{8}$ D $\frac{12}{8}$

28. Joanna came home from the store with $9\frac{1}{3}$ yards of fabric. How many yards of fabric was free?

FREE!

1/3 yard of fabric for every 2 yards you buy.

A $\frac{1}{3}$ yd   C 2 yd

B $1\frac{1}{3}$ yd   D 8 yd

Name _____

Circle the letter of the correct answer choice.

1. Graham parks these three cars in a row. Will they fit in a space that is $21\frac{1}{2}$ feet long?

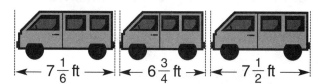

$\longleftarrow 7\frac{1}{6}$ ft $\longrightarrow$ $\longleftarrow 6\frac{3}{4}$ ft $\longrightarrow$ $\longleftarrow 7\frac{1}{2}$ ft $\longrightarrow$

A Yes; the cars measure $21\frac{5}{12}$ feet, which is less than $21\frac{1}{2}$ feet.

B Yes; the cars measure exactly $21\frac{1}{2}$ feet.

C No; the cars measure $21\frac{5}{12}$ feet, which is greater than $21\frac{1}{2}$ feet.

D No; the cars measure $21\frac{7}{12}$ feet, which is greater than $21\frac{1}{2}$ feet.

2. Compute.

$$5^2 + \frac{3}{4} - (2^3 - 3) \times 2$$

A $\frac{3}{4}$ **C** $15\frac{3}{4}$

B $12\frac{3}{4}$ **D** $41\frac{1}{2}$

3. What is $-\frac{9}{12}$ expressed in lowest terms?

A $0.6\overline{6}$ **C** $-\frac{2}{3}$

B 0.75 **D** $-\frac{3}{4}$

4. Compute.

$$\frac{3}{8} + 0.125 + \frac{1}{4}$$

A 0 **C** $\frac{3}{4}$

B $\frac{5}{8}$ **D** 1

5. Which answer choice shows these rational numbers in order from *least* to *greatest*?

A $-\frac{2}{3}, 0.5, -1\frac{1}{8}, -0.07$

B $-0.07, 0.5, -\frac{2}{3}, -1\frac{1}{8}$

C $0.5, -0.07, -\frac{2}{3}, -1\frac{1}{8}$

D $-1\frac{1}{8}, -\frac{2}{3}, -0.07, 0.5$

6. Which number does point *M* represent on the number line?

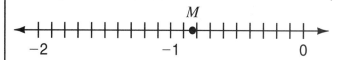

A -0.41 **C** $-\frac{100}{82}$

B $-\frac{41}{50}$ **D** 1.82

7. What value of *p* makes the equation true?

$$p - \frac{3}{4} = -1$$

A $-1\frac{3}{4}$ **C** $\frac{1}{4}$

B $-\frac{1}{4}$ **D** $1\frac{3}{4}$

8. Compute.

$$5\frac{1}{2} - 1\frac{1}{2} + 2 \times 3^2 - (14 \div 2)$$

A 4

B 15

C 53

D 65

9. What is *m* if $m + (^-1) = \frac{1}{8}$?

A $-1\frac{1}{8}$

C $\frac{7}{8}$

B $-\frac{7}{8}$

D $1\frac{1}{8}$

10. Identify the sign of the product in this multiplication problem.

$$-\frac{1}{4} \times -\frac{3}{8} = ?$$

A positive; because both factors are negative

B negative; because both factors are negative

C positive; because all negative fractions can be written as terminating decimals

D result is zero; you cannot multiply negative fractions

11. The low temperature in a town one day was $3\frac{1}{2}°$C. What was the approximate temperature in °F?
(Hint: °F ≈ 2 × °C + 30)

A 30°F

C 37°F

B 32°F

D 40°F

12. If $-\frac{1}{2} + z = 2$, what is the value of *z*?

$$-\frac{1}{2} + z = 2$$

A $-2\frac{1}{2}$

C $1\frac{1}{2}$

B $-1\frac{1}{2}$

D $2\frac{1}{2}$

13. Identify the sign of the quotient in this division problem.

$$2 \div -1\frac{1}{2} = ?$$

A positive; because the dividend and divisor have unlike signs

B negative; because the dividend and divisor have unlike signs

C negative; because all negative fractions can be written as repeating decimals

D result is zero; you cannot divide a whole number by a negative mixed number

14. Angel pours $3\frac{1}{2}$ cups of milk and $1\frac{3}{8}$ cups of water in a 6-cup measuring cup. Then she pours off $1\frac{1}{4}$ cups of the total before adding $2\frac{3}{4}$ cups of buttermilk. Will all of the liquid fit in the measuring cup?

A yes; $5\frac{3}{8} < 6$

B yes; $5\frac{7}{8} < 6$

C no; $6\frac{1}{8} > 6$

D no; $6\frac{3}{8} > 6$

Read the questions. Use the strategies to choose the answer choice that makes the most sense.

STRATEGIES

1. Janet is making oatmeal raisin cookies. The recipe calls for $\frac{3}{4}$ c of raisins. She only wants to make $\frac{2}{3}$ as many cookies as the recipe makes. How many cups of raisins does she need?

  A $\frac{1}{4}$ c **C** $\frac{1}{2}$ c

  B $\frac{2}{3}$ c **D** $1\frac{2}{3}$ c

Think
You can multiply a fraction and a fraction or a fraction and a whole number.

To answer this question, you need to find $\frac{2}{3}$ of $\frac{3}{4}$. You need to multiply $\frac{3}{4} \times \frac{2}{3}$.

- Multiply. $\frac{3}{4} \times \frac{2}{3} = \frac{6}{12}$

  simplest form → $\frac{1}{2}$

Remember: To multiply a fraction and a whole number, rename the whole number as a fraction with a denominator of 1.

Answer choice C is correct.

2. A turkey contains $3\frac{3}{8}$ servings per pound. How many servings can be made from a $5\frac{1}{3}$ lb turkey?

  A $15\frac{1}{2}$ **C** 17

  B $16\frac{3}{4}$ **D** 18

To answer this question, multiply $3\frac{3}{8} \times 5\frac{1}{3}$.

- Write the mixed numbers as fractions.

$$3\frac{3}{8} \times 5\frac{1}{3} = \frac{27}{8} \times \frac{16}{3}$$

- Simplify using the GCF.

$$\overset{9}{\underset{1}{\cancel{\frac{27}{8}}}} \times \overset{2}{\underset{1}{\cancel{\frac{16}{3}}}}$$

Think
GCF of 3 and 27: 3
GCF of 8 and 16: 3

- Multiply. $\frac{9}{1} \times \frac{2}{1} = \frac{18}{1}$
- Rename the product as a whole number.

Answer choice D is correct.

3. Roberto has $\frac{3}{4}$ yd of ribbon. How many $\frac{1}{8}$-yd pieces can he cut the ribbon into?

  A 3 pieces **C** 6 pieces

  B 4 pieces **D** 12 pieces

To answer this question, divide $\frac{3}{4} \div \frac{1}{8}$.

- Multiply by the reciprocal of the divisor.

$$\frac{3}{4} \div \frac{1}{8} = \frac{3}{4} \times \frac{8}{1}$$

Think
Reciprocal of $\frac{1}{8}$ is 8, or $\frac{8}{1}$.

- Multiply the numerators and denominators.

$$\frac{3}{4} \times \frac{8}{1} = \frac{24}{4}$$

- Rename the product as a whole number. $\frac{24}{4} = 6$

Answer choice C is correct.

Circle the letter of the correct answer choice.

4. Katrina missed $\frac{1}{5}$ of the questions on her math test. She corrected $\frac{3}{4}$ of the questions she missed. What fraction of the questions on the test did she correct?

A $\frac{1}{2}$

B $\frac{4}{9}$

C $\frac{1}{20}$

D $\frac{3}{20}$

5. Divide: $\frac{4}{7} \div \frac{1}{14}$

A $\frac{1}{8}$ C 8

B $\frac{56}{8}$ D $\frac{2}{49}$

6. A box of frozen hamburgers contains $6\frac{3}{4}$ lb of meat. At the Johnson family reunion, they used $4\frac{2}{3}$ boxes. How many pounds of meat did they use at the reunion?

A $1\frac{25}{56}$ lb

B $11\frac{5}{12}$ lb

C $24\frac{1}{2}$ lb

D $31\frac{1}{2}$ lb

7. A chef uses a pancake recipe that needs $1\frac{2}{3}$ c of sugar for each batch of pancakes she makes. How much sugar is needed if she makes 24 batches of pancakes?

A $\frac{1}{40}$ c   C 8 c

B $10\frac{2}{3}$ c   D 40 c

8. Mr. Green's math classroom has 35 desks arranged in rows of 5 desks each. How many students does Mr. Green have in his math class if $\frac{4}{5}$ of $\frac{6}{7}$ of the desks are occupied?

A 24 students   C 30 students

B 28 students   D 35 students

9. Find the product. $\frac{4}{5} \times \frac{2}{3} \times \frac{5}{9}$

A $\frac{40}{127}$

B $\frac{9}{26}$

C $\frac{8}{27}$

D $\frac{13}{17}$

10. Will has 4 lb of peanuts. He wants to put them in bags so that there is $\frac{2}{3}$ lb in each bag. How many bags can he fill?

A 4 bags   C 8 bags

B 6 bags   D 12 bags

Read the questions. Use the strategies to choose the answer choice that makes the most sense.

STRATEGIES

---

1. Bill has 30 yd of fabric to make banners for the football cheering section. He will use $3\frac{3}{4}$ yd of fabric for each banner. How many banners can he make?

  A 10

  B $112\frac{1}{2}$

  C 8

  D $22\frac{1}{2}$

Remember: To divide fractions, you multiply the dividend by the reciprocal of the divisor.

You need to divide 30 yd by $3\frac{3}{4}$.

• Rename the whole number as the fraction $\frac{30}{1}$.

• Rename the mixed number $3\frac{3}{4}$ as the fraction $\frac{15}{4}$.

• Dividend = $\frac{30}{1}$. Divisor = $\frac{15}{4}$. Reciprocal = $\frac{4}{15}$.

• Multiply $\frac{30}{1}$ by $\frac{4}{15}$. → $\overset{2}{\cancel{\frac{30}{1}}} \times \frac{4}{\underset{1}{\cancel{15}}} \to \frac{2}{1} \times \frac{4}{1} = \frac{8}{1}$.

• Write the quotient in simplest form: $\frac{8}{1} = 8$

Answer choice C is correct.

---

2. Evaluate the expression $b \div \frac{4}{7}$, when $b = 18$.

  A $10\frac{2}{7}$

  B $31\frac{1}{2}$

  C 32

  D $32\frac{1}{2}$

• Replace the variable with the given value.

$$18 \div \frac{4}{7} = \frac{18}{1} \div \frac{4}{7}$$

• Multiply by the reciprocal of the divisor. Then simplify if possible.

$$\frac{\overset{9}{\cancel{18}}}{1} \times \frac{7}{\underset{2}{\cancel{4}}} = \frac{9}{1} \times \frac{7}{2}$$

• Multiply the numerators. Then multiply the denominators.

$$\frac{9 \times 7}{1 \times 2} = \frac{63}{2}$$

• Write the quotient in simplest form: $\frac{63}{2} = 31\frac{1}{2}$

Answer choice B is correct.

---

3. Solve: $\frac{2}{8}y + \frac{3}{8}y = \frac{11}{12}$

  A $y = 1$ **C** $y = 1\frac{2}{15}$

  B $y = \frac{55}{96}$ **D** $y = 1\frac{7}{15}$

To solve the equation. $\frac{2}{8}y + \frac{3}{8}y = \frac{11}{12}$:

• $\frac{5}{8}y = \frac{11}{12}$ ◄— combine like terms

• $\frac{5}{8}y \div \frac{5}{8} = \frac{11}{12} \div \frac{5}{8}$ ◄— isolate the variable

• $y = \frac{11}{\underset{3}{\cancel{12}}} \times \frac{\overset{2}{\cancel{8}}}{5} = \frac{22}{15} = 1\frac{7}{15}$ ◄— compute to solve

└─ simplest form

Answer choice D is correct.

Name _____

Circle the letter of the correct answer choice.

4. Use the Order of Operations to simplify:

$\frac{1}{12} + \frac{1}{4} \times 12$

A $\frac{1}{4}$

B $3\frac{1}{12}$

C 4

D $6\frac{1}{12}$

5. Solve: $\frac{6}{11}b = 7\frac{1}{5}$

A $b = 12\frac{1}{5}$

B $b = 13$

C $b = 13\frac{1}{5}$

D $b = 14\frac{4}{5}$

Which expression could you use to answer this question?

6. The woodworking class has a board that they cut into $3\frac{1}{2}$-ft pieces. If the board is 21 ft long, how many pieces do they cut?

A $b \div 3\frac{1}{2}$, when $b = 21$

B $b \div 21$, when $b = 3\frac{1}{2}$

C $b \times 3\frac{1}{2}$, when $b = 21$

D $3\frac{1}{2} \div b$, when $b = 21$

7. Solve for x. $x \div \frac{4}{5} = \frac{1}{12}$

A $x = \frac{1}{15}$

B $x = \frac{5}{48}$

C $x = \frac{4}{75}$

D $x = 1\frac{1}{15}$

8. Solve for m. $m \times \frac{2}{3} = 2\frac{1}{2}$

A $m = 1\frac{2}{3}$

B $m = 3\frac{3}{4}$

C $m = 4\frac{1}{6}$

D $m = \frac{3}{4}$

9. Use the Order of Operations to simplify:

$\left(\frac{2}{7} + \frac{1}{3}\right) \times 12$

A 7   C $8\frac{3}{7}$

B $7\frac{3}{7}$ D $1\frac{1}{7}$

10. Solve for p: $3p + \frac{3}{5}p = 2\frac{1}{10}$

A $p = \frac{21}{16}$ C $p = \frac{5}{12}$

B $p = 1\frac{1}{2}$ D $p = \frac{7}{12}$

Read the questions. Use the strategies to choose the answer choice that makes the most sense.

STRATEGIES

1. Find $P(> 4)$.

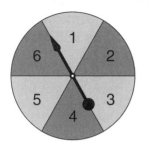

   A $\frac{1}{6}$ **C** $\frac{1}{3}$

   B $\frac{1}{4}$ **D** 2

• You need to find the probability of the spinner landing on a number greater than 4.

$$P(E) = \frac{\text{number of favorable outcomes}}{\text{total number of possible outcomes}}$$

$$P(E) = \frac{2}{6} = \frac{1}{3}$$

Think
There are 6 possible outcomes—1, 2, 3, 4, 5, and 6. The favorable outcomes are 5 and 6.

Answer choice C is correct.

---

2. **How many ways can you arrange 3 of 4 books in any order on a shelf?**

   A 4

   B 6

   C 12

   D 24

• The order does not matter, so find the number of combinations.

$4 \times 3 \times 2 \times 1 = 24 \longleftarrow$ permutations

$3 \times 2 \times 1 = 6 \longleftarrow$ arrangements

$24 \div 6 = 4$

Think
Divide the number of permutations by the number of arrangements for each combination.

Answer choice A is correct.

---

3. **Jack has a coin and a bag containing one red, one blue, and one green marble. What is the probability of tossing heads and pulling out a red marble from the bag?**

   A $\frac{1}{6}$ **C** $\frac{1}{2}$

   B $\frac{1}{3}$ **D** $\frac{5}{6}$

• Write the probability of each independent event as a fraction.

$$P(\text{heads}) = \frac{1}{2}$$

$$P(\text{red}) = \frac{1}{3}$$

Think
The probability of a compound event is the product of the probabilities of each event.

$$P(\text{heads, red}) \frac{1}{2} \times \frac{1}{3} = \frac{1}{6}$$

Answer choice A is correct.

Name _____

Circle the letter of the correct answer choice.

4. How likely are you to spin an even number on the spinner below?

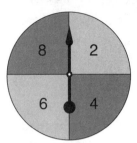

A impossible

B unlikely

C likely

D certain

5. Look at the spinner in Problem 4. What is P (multiple of 3)?

A 0

C $\frac{3}{4}$

B $\frac{1}{4}$

D 1

6. The table shows the results of pulling a marble from a bag. The marble was replaced after each pull. What is the probability that the next marble pulled from the bag will be green?

Color	Number of Pulls
White	6
Yellow	10
Green	4

A $\frac{1}{5}$

C $\frac{1}{2}$

B $\frac{1}{4}$

D $\frac{3}{4}$

7. David has 3 black shirts and 3 white shirts in a drawer. He has 1 red tie and 1 yellow tie in the closet. If he picks a shirt and a tie at random what is the probability that he will pick a black shirt with a yellow tie?

A $\frac{1}{8}$

C $\frac{1}{4}$

B $\frac{1}{6}$

D 1

8. Six students want to represent Mr. Vega's class on the student council. He can choose 2 students. How many different pairs of students can Mr. Vega choose from?

A 12

B 15

C 22

D 30

9. Maya has 2 bus tokens, 2 game tokens, and 2 coins in her pocket. All of the objects are all the same size, shape, and weight. If Maya picks one object from her pocket without looking, what is the probability that it will *not* be a coin?

A $\frac{2}{3}$

C $\frac{1}{3}$

B $\frac{1}{2}$

D $\frac{1}{6}$

10. On a number cube labeled 1–6, what is the probability of rolling the number 2?

A $\frac{1}{2}$

C $\frac{1}{5}$

B $\frac{1}{3}$

D $\frac{1}{6}$

Read the questions. Use the strategies to choose the answer choice that makes the most sense.

STRATEGIES

1. **Which is the best way to survey students to get their opinions about their favorite sport?**

   A Ask the captain of the football team to name his favorite sport.

   B Ask the members of the soccer team which sport they play.

   C Ask 5 students in each class to name a sport that they play.

   D Ask 5 students in each class to name their favorite sport.

Remember: A sample group surveyed should represent everyone. If certain groups are not represented then the sample is not fair.

Analyze the questions. Are they fair?

A: The right question asked to the wrong person.

B: Members of the soccer team will say soccer.

C: A good sample group, but a bad question.

D: This question correctly surveys a representative sample of the school. It asks a random, unbiased question.

Answer choice D is correct.

2. **What is the mode number of students in a class at Jefferson Elementary?**

Class size: Jefferson Elementary School				
24	22	26	25	24
28	26	25	26	27
23	25	26	27	24
23	24	26	25	23

   A 24   **C** 26

   B 25   **D** 28

• Organize data into a relative frequency list or table.

```
22
23  23  23
24  24  24  24
25  25  25  25
26  26  26  26  26
27  27
28
```

Think
The mode is the number that occurs most often.

Answer choice C is correct.

3. **What effect does the outlier have on the mean of this data?**

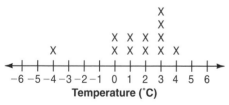

   Temperature (°C)

   A The outlier lowers the mean.

   B The outlier raises the mean.

   C The outlier has no effect on the mean.

   D The data has no outlier.

Remember: Outliers are numbers set apart from the rest of the data. They can affect how you interpret your data.

• Identify the outlier. ⟶ −4°C.

• Find the mean with the outlier. **mean = average**
   $-4 + 0 + 0 + 1 + 1 + 2 + 2 + 3 + 3 + 3 + 3 + 4 = 18$
   $18 \div 12 = 1.5$ ◄— mean with outlier

• Calculate the mean without the outlier.
   $0 + 0 + 1 + 1 + 2 + 2 + 3 + 3 + 3 + 3 + 4 = 22$
   $22 \div 11 = 2$ ◄— mean without the outlier

Answer choice A is correct.

Circle the letter of the correct answer choice.

4. **Which of these survey questions is unbiased?**

   A Is Spanish the easiest language to learn?

   B Isn't the beach the best place for vacation?

   C What is the most important trait in a friend?

   D Is it right to give students more than two hours of homework per night?

5. **What effect does the outlier have on the mean of this data?**

Number of Books Owned	
Name	**Number**
Michael	50
Jasmine	65
Hunter	40
Grace	100
Julia	85
Benjamin	45
Timothy	55

   A The outlier lowers the mean.

   B The outlier raises the mean.

   C The outlier has no effect on the mean.

   D The data has no outlier.

6. **In the past 7 days, Lena picked the following number of tomatoes from her garden: 3, 1, 4, 5, 2, 4, 2. What is the mean number of tomatoes picked?**

   A 2   C 5

   B 3   D 21

7. **If 32 hats are sold on Saturday, how would the mode change?**

Hat Sales Per Day				
Mon.	**Tues.**	**Wed.**	**Thurs.**	**Fri.**
24	17	29	29	11

   A The mode would decrease.

   B The mode would increase.

   C The mode would stay the same.

   D The new data set would have no mode

8. **Laura wants to know the most common way that students get to school. Which method will give the most accurate results?**

   A select 10 students from each homeroom

   B select students putting bikes in a rack

   C select students leaving the school bus

   D select a family of brothers and sisters

9. **Ralph takes a survey to determine the most popular rock band in town. Which of the following represents the *best* way for him to choose a random sample?**

   A people leaving a rock concert

   B shoppers at a classical music store

   C students in his math class

   D people at the local shopping center

Read the questions. Use the strategies to choose
the answer choice that makes the most sense.

1. The data in this stem-and-leaf plot was used to create the box-and-whisker plot. Which is the lower quartile of the box and whisker plot?

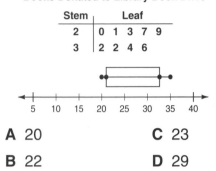

Books Donated to Library Book Drive

Stem	Leaf
2	0 1 3 7 9
3	2 2 4 6

A 20

B 22

C 23

D 29

- Order the data from $<$ to $>$. Identify the median or middle number of ordered data.

- Find the middle values, or median, of the numbers before and after the median of all the data.

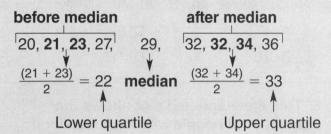

before median

after median

20, **21**, **23**, 27,   29,   32, **32**, **34**, 36

$\frac{(21 + 23)}{2} = 22$ **median** $\frac{(32 + 34)}{2} = 33$

Lower quartile   Upper quartile

Answer choice B is correct.

---

2. **About what was the greatest difference between sales of baseballs and footballs?**

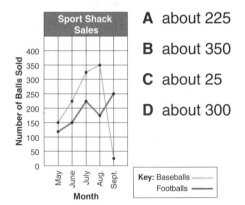

A about 225

B about 350

C about 25

D about 300

> **Think**
> Each line in a double line graph shows a separate data set.

- Read the key, then find the line that represents each kind of ball.
- The lines show that the greatest difference between types of balls is in September.
- Find the approximate value of each point in September.
  Baseballs Sold: 25   Footballs Sold: 250
- Subtract: $250 - 25 = 225$

Answer choice A is correct.

---

3. **Which number represents about how much more chocolate ice-cream was sold than vanilla?**

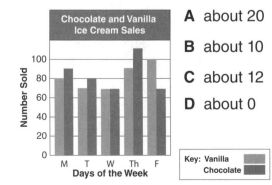

A about 20

B about 10

C about 12

D about 0

- Use the key to determine which color bar represents each flavor.
- Find the place on the graph where each bar stops.
- Use the scale that shows the number sold to determine the amount sold.

Add chocolate: $90 + 80 + 70 + 110 + 70 = 420$
Add vanilla: $80 + 70 + 70 + 90 + 100 = 410$
- Subtract: $420 - 410 = 10$

Answer choice B is correct.

Name _____

Circle the letter of the correct answer choice.

4. What is the upper quartile of the data shown here?

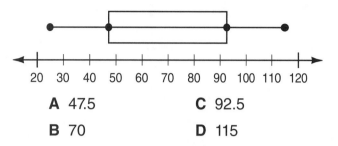

A 47.5   **C** 92.5

B 70   **D** 115

5. This stem-and-leaf plot shows the number of people who took a college campus tour. What is the range of the data?

Stem	Leaf
2	0 3 3 6
3	1 1 2 5
4	0 1 2 7 7

A 2   **C** 32

B 27   **D** 67

6. In a double line graph showing monthly boot and shoe sales at a store, how would a drop in sales of both be shown?

A two horizontal lines

B two lines crossing to make an X

C two lines sloping up from left to right

D two lines sloping down from left to right

7. In which month was there the greatest difference between sandal and sneaker sales?

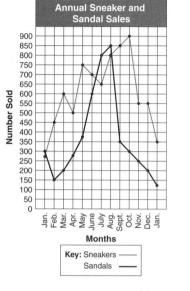

A May   **C** June

B October   **D** September

8. The double bar graph shows the number of shoes sold last month at three shoe shops.

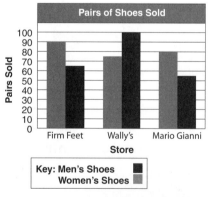

How many more pair of men's shoes did Firm Feet and Wally's sell than Mario Gianni?

A 165   **C** 80

B 110   **D** 18

Read the questions. Use the strategies to choose the answer choice that makes the most sense.

1. How can this graph be changed to make monthly sales look stronger than they are?

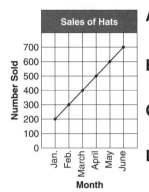

A Expand the vertical scale.

B Shrink the vertical scale.

C Expand the horizontal scale.

D Shrink the horizontal scale.

• Expand the vertical scale so that the graph gives the impression that sales are stronger than they are.

Think
If the line rises up steeply from left to right, sales will look strong and fast.

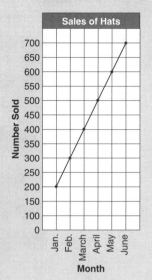

Answer choice A is correct.

---

2. The histogram shows the number of days some students spent reading last summer. How many students were surveyed?

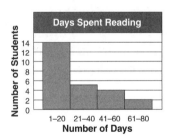

A 5   **C** 23

B 14   **D** 25

A histogram is a graph that shows the *frequency* of equal intervals of the data.

• Identify the number of students in each interval.

1–20 days: 14

21–40 days: 5

41–60 days: 4

61–80 days: 2

Think
You can also make a frequency table of the data to solve this problem.

• Add.

$14 + 5 + 4 + 2 = 25$

Answer choice D is correct.

---

3. There are 60 boats at the lake. How many more motorboats are there than dinghies?

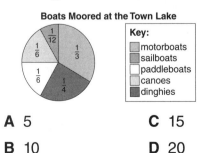

A 5   **C** 15

B 10   **D** 20

Remember: A circle graph relates parts of a set to the whole. The parts may be given as fractions or percents.

• Multiply the fraction for each category by the total number.

Motorboats: $\frac{1}{3} \times 60 = 20$

Dinghies: $\frac{1}{4} \times 60 = 15$

• Subtract to compare. $20 - 15 = 5$

Answer choice A is correct.

Name _____

Circle the letter of the correct answer choice.

4. **How does this graph mislead viewers about the information it shows?**

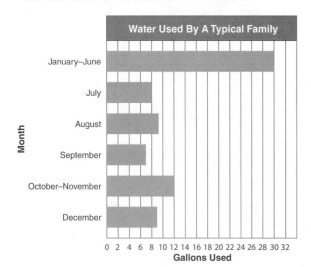

Water Used By A Typical Family

Month

January–June

July

August

September

October–November

December

0 2 4 6 8 10 12 14 16 18 20 22 24 26 28 30 32
Gallons Used

   A The scale is in units of 2.

   B The data only represents one year.

   C Each bar does not represent the same interval of time.

   D September and December are the same.

Use the histogram below for Questions 5 and 6.

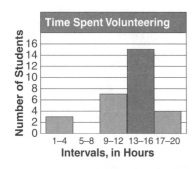

Time Spent Volunteering

Number of Students

16
14
12
10
8
6
4
2
0

1–4 5–8 9–12 13–16 17–20
Intervals, in Hours

5. **How many students were surveyed?**

   A 15   C 29

   B 20   D 32

6. **Which interval has the least frequency?**

   A 1–4 h

   B 5–8 h

   C 13–16 h

   D 17–20 h

Use the circle graph below for Questions 7 and 8.

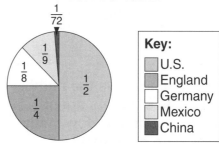

Coins in an International Coin Collection

$\frac{1}{72}$

$\frac{1}{9}$

$\frac{1}{8}$

$\frac{1}{2}$

$\frac{1}{4}$

Key:
   ☐ U.S.
   ■ England
   ☐ Germany
   ☐ Mexico
   ■ China

7. **There are 72 coins in this collection. How many more coins are there from England than there are from Germany and Mexico combined?**

   A 1   C 18

   B 17   D 35

8. **If 18 of the U.S. coins were lost, which statement would be true?**

   A There would be a total of 90 coins.

   B $\frac{1}{4}$ of the coins in the collection would be from the U.S.

   C Germany, Mexico, and the U.S. would have the same number of coins.

   D The English money would make up $\frac{1}{3}$ of the collection.

Read the questions. Use the strategies to choose the answer choice that makes the most sense.

1. Lines *AB* and *CD* are parallel. Which statement about the diagram is true?

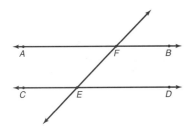

A ∠*AFE* is obtuse.

B $\overleftrightarrow{AB} \parallel \overleftrightarrow{EF}$

C $\overleftrightarrow{AB} \perp \overleftrightarrow{CD}$

D ∠*DEF* is acute.

Remember: ∥ means parallel. ⊥ means perpendicular. Acute angles measure < 90°. Obtuse angles measure > 90°.

A: ∠*AFE* measures less than 90°, so it is an acute angle.

B: $\overleftrightarrow{AB}$ and $\overleftrightarrow{EF}$ intersect, so they cannot be parallel.

C: $\overleftrightarrow{AB}$ and $\overleftrightarrow{CD}$ do not intersect, so they are not perpendicular.

D: ∠*DEF* measures less than 90°, so it is acute.

Answer choice D is correct.

---

2. In the figure below, if m∠1 = 115°, what is the measure of ∠8?

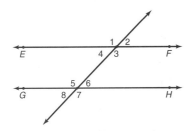

A 65°   **C** 115°

B 90°   **D** 180°

• Identify the relationships between the pairs of angles in the diagram.

Angles 1 and 4 are supplementary.

Angles 4 and 8 are corresponding angles.

• Find the measures of the angles.

m∠1 + m∠4 = 180°
115° + m∠4 = 180°
m∠4 = 65°

m∠4 = m∠8
m∠8 = 65°

Remember: The sum of the measures of supplementary angles is 180°. Corresponding angles are congruent.

Answer choice A is correct.

---

3. ∠*QPS* and ∠*SPT* are congruent. Which ray is an angle bisector?

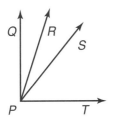

A $\overrightarrow{PQ}$ **C** $\overrightarrow{PS}$

B $\overrightarrow{PR}$ **D** $\overrightarrow{PT}$

• Find a ray that makes two congruent angles.

$\overrightarrow{PQ}$ and $\overrightarrow{PT}$ are external rays on an angle. They do not bisect another angle.

$\overrightarrow{PR}$ divides ∠*QPT*, but does not bisect it.

$\overrightarrow{PS}$ divides ∠*QPT* into congruent angles.

Think
Ray *PR* is not a bisector because ∠*QPR* and ∠*RPT* are not congruent.

Answer choice C is correct.

Circle the letter of the correct answer choice.

---

4. **What is the measure of ∠1?**

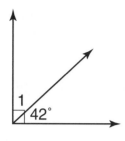

    A 42°   **C** 90°

    B 48°   **D** 138°

---

5. **Which angle is obtuse?**

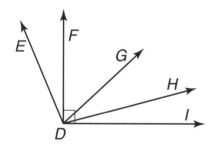

    A ∠IDH   **C** ∠HDG

    B ∠IDF   **D** ∠EDI

---

6. **∠QAM measures 50°. Which other angle has the same measure?**

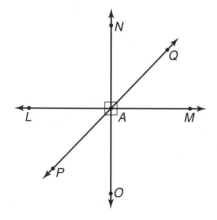

    A ∠NAQ   **C** ∠LAP

    B ∠MAO   **D** ∠OAP

In this figure, lines *RS* and *TU* are parallel. Use the figure for Exercises 7–9.

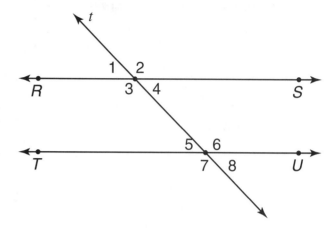

7. **Which statement is true?**

    A ∠1 and ∠3 are vertical angles.

    B ∠2 and ∠7 are alternate exterior angles.

    C ∠5 and ∠3 are corresponding angles.

    D ∠3 and ∠6 are alternate exterior angles.

8. **If m∠5 is 79°, what is the measure of ∠7?**

    A 11°   **C** 101°

    B 79°   **D** 180°

9. **The measure of ∠2 is 130°. What is the measure of ∠5?**

    A 40°   **C** 90°

    B 50°   **D** 130°

Read the questions. Use the strategies to choose
the answer choice that makes the most sense.

STRATEGIES

**1. Which type of figure would be
similar to the one shown here?**

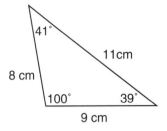

A isosceles right triangle

B quadrilateral

C equilateral triangle

D scalene obtuse triangle

• Look at the sides and angles to identify the figure.

The figure has 3 sides so it is a triangle.

None of the sides are congruent, so it is scalene.

The triangle has an obtuse angle.

A figure similar to this one is a scalene obtuse
triangle.

·Think·
Similar figures have the same shape, but may
have a different size.

Answer choice D is correct.

---

2. Find the value of x.

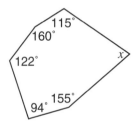

A 74° **C** 646°

B 122° **D** 794°

• Count the sides of the polygon to find the sum of
the measure of its interior angles.

$(n - 2) \times 180°$

$(6 - 2) \times 180°$

$4 \times 180° = 720°$

·Think·
Three diagonals drawn from a vertex
of a hexagon make 4 triangles.
So the sum of the interior angles is
$4 \times 180° = 720°$.

$94° + 155° + 122° + 160° + 115° + x° = 720°$

$646° + x° = 720°$

$x = 74°$

Answer choice A is correct.

**3. Point E is the center of the circle
shown here. If SR measures 24 in.,
what is the length of ET?**

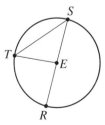

A 2 in. **C** 8 in.

B 4 in. **D** 12 in.

• Identify the parts of the circle.

$\overline{SR}$ is a diameter.

$\overline{TE}$ is a radius.

·Think·
The length of the radius of a
circle is half the length of the
diameter.

radius = diameter ÷ 2

length $\overline{ET} = 24 ÷ 2 = 12$ inches

Answer choice D is correct.

Name _____

Circle the letter of the correct answer choice.

4. Which figure is an obtuse triangle?

5. An isosceles triangle has sides that measure 3 in. and 4 in. What could be the measure of the third side?

A 1 inch   **C** 3 inches

B 2 inches   **D** 7 inches

6. The tiles in Sarah's bathroom are 4-sided polygons with exactly one pair of parallel sides. What shape are the tiles?

A trapezoid   **C** rhombus

B square   **D** rectangle

7. What is the measure of _n_ in this quadrilateral?

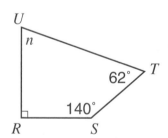

A 68°   **C** 158°

B 90°   **D** 292°

8. Which polygon has interior angles with a sum of 1080°?

A pentagon

B hexagon

C heptagon

D octagon

9. In this diagram, _C_ is the center of the circle. If _GC_ measures 5 cm, which other segment has the same length?

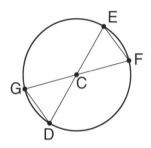

A $\overline{GD}$ **C** $\overset{\frown}{GE}$

B $\overline{GF}$ **D** $\overline{CD}$

10. Quadrilaterals _WXYZ_ and _NOPQ_ are congruent. ∠Z and ∠Q have the same measure. Which answer choice identifies corresponding parts?

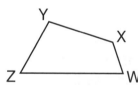
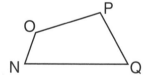

A $\overline{ZY}$ and $\overline{NO}$

B ∠W and ∠N

C ∠X and ∠P

D $\overline{XY}$ and $\overline{NQ}$

Read the questions. Use the strategies to choose the answer choice that makes the most sense.

---

1. What type of symmetry does this figure have?

A reflection

B rotation

C point

D none

• Draw the lines of symmetry on the figure.

> Remember: A figure has **reflection symmetry** if the line or lines of symmetry create mirror images on either side of the lines.

Answer choice A is correct.

---

2. In this tessellation, how is the shaded figure transformed?

A translations only

B reflections only

C reflections and rotations

D translations and reflections

• Look at how the figure changes in the tessellation.

The figure below the shaded figure is a reflection. The figure to the right of the shaded figure is a rotation.

Look for other reflections and rotations.

> **Think**
> When a figure is reflected, a mirror image is formed. When a figure is rotated, it turns around a point.

Answer choice C is correct.

---

3. If this net were folded, what solid figure would it make?

A cone

B triangular pyramid

C triangular prism

D square pyramid

• Look at each answer choice.

A: A cone has a circular base.

B: A triangular pyramid does not have a square base.

> Remember: A net shows the shapes of the base and sides of a solid figure.

C: A net for a triangular prism has 2 congruent triangles and rectangles.

• Eliminate answer choices **A**, **B**, and **C**.

D: A net for a square pyramid has a square base and 4 triangles.

Answer choice D is correct.
The net would fold into a square pyramid.

Circle the letter of the correct answer choice.

4. **Which pair of figures shows a translation?**

A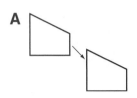

B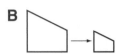

C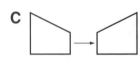

D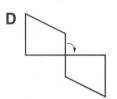

5. **What kind of symmetry is shown by this letter?**

   A rotation   C point

   B reflection   D reverse

6. **Which of these figures shows rotation symmetry in a $\frac{1}{6}$, or 60°, turn?**

A

B

C

D

7. **Which of these figures will *not* tessellate?**

A

B

C

D

8. **Identify this figure.**

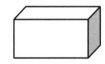

   A cube

   B hexagonal prism

   C rectangular prism

   D rectangular pyramid

9. **Which of these figures has 4 faces, 6 edges, and 4 vertices?**

A   C

B   D

10. **What shape is any face, other than the base, of a square pyramid?**

   A triangle   C rectangle

   B square   D pentagon

Read the problem. Use the Problem-Solving Guide below to help you think about the answer choices.

A wheel used in a factory has a diameter of 6 ft and makes a complete revolution every 2 minutes. About how many feet will it travel in 30 minutes?

A 141.3 ft   **C** 282.6 ft

B 226.08 ft   **D** 1695.6 ft

PROBLEM-SOLVING GUIDE

1 Understand the Question

- The question is asking you to find the answer choice that shows the distance a wheel will travel in 30 minutes.
- Each answer choice gives a distance measurement in feet.

2 Understand Word Meanings

- You may know the word *revolution* from your Social Studies classes. It is a multiple-meaning word, and can be defined as "overthrowing or replacing a government." However, by reading the context of the word problem, here the word *revolution* is being applied to mechanics and is defined as, "a circular turn that travels the full distance of the circle's circumference or length."

3 Understand How to Solve

- Reread the question if you need to.
- First, calculate the wheel's circumference to find its approximate length.

$$C = \pi d \longrightarrow 3.14 \times 6 \approx 18.84 \text{ ft}$$

- Then, multiply the circumference, or the distance in feet around the circle, by 15 which is the number of complete revolutions made by the wheel in 30 minutes.

18.84 ft × 15 = 282.60 ft

Think
Since the wheel will travel its entire *circumference* every 2 minutes, you must divide 30 minutes by 2. This answer will give you the number of full revolutions made in 30 minutes.

4 Circle the Letter of the Correct Answer Choice.

Answer choice C is correct.
The wheel will travel 282.6 ft in 30 minutes.

Name _____

Circle the letter of the correct answer choice.

This table shows the results of pulling a marble from a bag without looking and then putting it back. What is the likelihood that the next marble pulled will be red?

Color	Number of Pulls
Red	10
White	12
Blue	3

A $\frac{2}{3}$ **C** $\frac{1}{10}$

B $\frac{2}{5}$ **D** $\frac{1}{25}$

Complete each sentence.

1 **Understand the Question**

• The table shows the number of _____ for each _____ .

• The question is asking you to find the answer choice that names the _____ that the

next marble pulled will be _____ .

• Each answer choice is a _____ that shows the _____ .

2 **Understand Word Meanings: likelihood**

• You know that the word **likely** means "a good chance of happening."
• You know that when the suffix **-hood** is added it means "the state of."

• Write what you think *likelihood* means. _____

3 **Understand How to Solve**

• First find the denominator, or total number of _____ : _____ .

• Next find the numerator, or the number of times a _____ marble was pulled: _____.

• Finally, write and simplify the fraction: $\frac{10}{25}$ = _____ .

4 **Circle the Letter of the Correct Answer Choice.**

Answer choice B is correct.

The likelihood of red is $\frac{2}{5}$.

Name _____

Circle the letter of the correct answer choice.

---

1. Andrew surveyed his class about the number of hours they slept this week. He made a box-and-whisker plot to show the results. Which statement about the data is *false*?

Number of hours slept

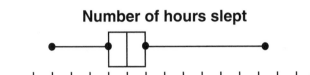

43 46 49 52 55 58 61 64 67 70 73 76 79 82 85

   A None of the students slept fewer than 46 hours.

   B Half of the students slept between 55 and 61 hours.

   C Only 2 students slept more than 80 hours.

   D One-fourth of the students slept 61 hours or more.

---

2. Corrine works for a landscaping company. She adds oil and gas to the lawn mowers. For every quart of gas, she adds a half of a cup of oil. How many cups of oil should she add with 12 quarts of gas?

   A $\frac{1}{6}$ cups

   B 6 cups

   C $12\frac{1}{2}$ cups

   D 6 quarts

---

3. It takes Joaquin $\frac{1}{3}$ of an hour to walk from his house to school. How many minutes does it take him to walk to school?

   A 20 minutes

   B $33\frac{1}{3}$ minutes

   C 40 minutes

   D 60 minutes

---

4. Milo is handing out flyers concerning the next election. The flyers are printed on colored paper: 20 pink, 30 yellow, and 25 blue, shuffled randomly. What are the *odds* in favor of Milo giving out a blue flyer?

   A $\frac{1}{3}$

   B $\frac{1}{2}$

   C $\frac{3}{5}$

   D $\frac{2}{3}$

---

5. The angle formed by adjacent angles *A* and *B* is a right angle. What is the measure of angle *A*?

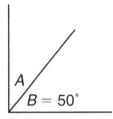

   A 40°

   B 50°

   C 90°

   D 130°

---

6. Henry's bread recipe calls for $7\frac{1}{2}$ cups of flour. The recipe makes three loaves. If Henry only wants to make one loaf, how much flour will he need?

A $\frac{1}{3}$ cup

B $2\frac{1}{2}$ cups

C $7\frac{1}{2}$ cups

D $22\frac{1}{2}$ cups

8. Use a protractor to find the measure of angle *MNO*.

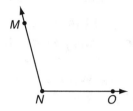

A 75°

B 95°

C 105°

D 120°

7. This circle graph shows the ages of customers at a popular music store. What percentage of the customers are ages 10–19?

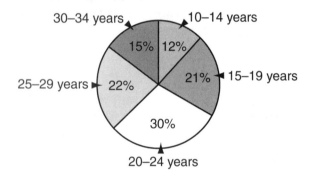

A 9%

B 12%

C 21%

D 33%

9. Gabriel is cutting a board into equal pieces to make birdhouses. The board is 12 ft long, and each piece is $\frac{3}{4}$ ft long. How many pieces can he cut from the board, if he uses the whole board?

A 1 piece

B 9 pieces

C 12 pieces

D 16 pieces

10. Segment *TU* is parallel to segment *VW*. What is the measure of angle *H*?

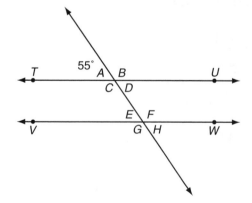

A 55°

B 110°

C 125°

D 180°

Name _____

Circle the letter of the correct answer choice.

---

11. Sophia writes down the height in inches of the students in her class:

$55\frac{1}{2}$	58	$57\frac{1}{4}$
57	$58\frac{1}{2}$	$56\frac{1}{2}$
61	$56\frac{1}{4}$	$61\frac{1}{2}$
62	58	57
56	$55\frac{3}{4}$	$56\frac{1}{4}$
$61\frac{1}{2}$	56	$58\frac{1}{4}$
56	59	$57\frac{3}{4}$

What is the median height of the students in the class?

A $55\frac{1}{2}$ inches

B 56 inches

C $57\frac{1}{4}$ inches

D 58 inches

---

12. Look again at the data in Exercise 11. What was the range of the heights?

A $2\frac{1}{4}$ inches

B $6\frac{1}{2}$ inches

C $7\frac{1}{2}$ inches

D $8\frac{1}{2}$ inches

---

13. An architect designs a circular pool like the one shown below. A rope will cut across the pool, through the center. In the architect's drawing, what is the measure of arc *POL*?

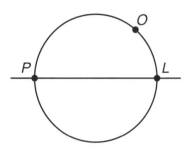

A 60°

B 120°

C 180°

D 360°

---

14. How many ways can you arrange 3 of 4 coffee cups in any order on a shelf?

A 4

B 8

C 12

D 24

---

15. Ethan has $1\frac{1}{2}$ lbs of sand. This is only $\frac{3}{4}$ as much as he needs to make a batch of concrete. How much sand is needed to make a batch of concrete?

A $\frac{3}{4}$ lb   **C** 2 lbs

B $1\frac{1}{8}$ lbs   **D** $2\frac{1}{4}$ lbs

---

16. Between which two days of the month was there the sharpest increase in high temperatures?

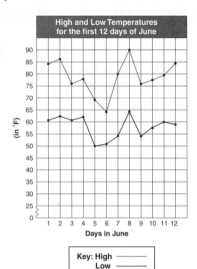

A June 4 and June 5

B June 6 and June 7

C June 13 and June 14

D June 14 and June 15

17. Look again at the graph in Exercise 16. What trend does the graph show?

A When the temperature was higher, there was more rain.

B When the temperature was lower, there was more rain.

C When the high temps were higher, the low temps were higher, too.

D When the high temps were higher, the low temps were lower.

18. Rory doodles this figure on a notebook. Which statement about the figure is *false*?

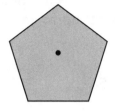

A The figure has rotational symmetry.

B The figure has more than one line of symmetry.

C The figure has five interior angles.

D The figure demonstrates a translation.

19. Isabella has 4 blue and 4 black jeans. She has 1 white and 1 yellow t-shirt. If she picks a pair of jeans and a t-shirt at random, what is the probability that she will wear a pair of blue jeans with the yellow t-shirt?

A $\frac{1}{4}$　　　　**C** $\frac{1}{8}$

B $\frac{1}{10}$　　　　**D** $\frac{1}{5}$

20. Paul packs candies in a box shaped like the figure below. What answer choice *best* describes the shape of the box?

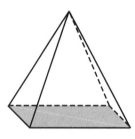

A rectangular prism

B triangular pyramid

C rectangular pyramid

D tetrahedron

Name _____

Circle the letter of the correct answer choice.

1. This graph shows the prizes Mrs. Rosa put in a party grab bag. What is the probability that the first person will pull out a pack of trading cards?

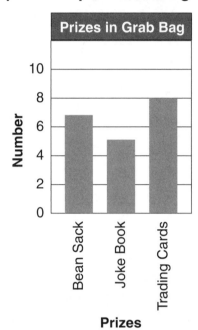

Prizes in Grab Bag

Number

Bean Sack Joke Book Trading Cards

Prizes

A $\frac{1}{8}$

B $\frac{2}{5}$

C $\frac{8}{15}$

D $\frac{3}{5}$

2. Find the value of *g*.

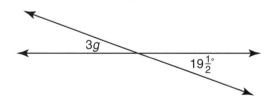

$3g$ $19\frac{1}{2}°$

A $6\frac{1}{2}°$ C $23\frac{1}{2}°$

B $19\frac{1}{2}°$ D $58\frac{1}{2}°$

3. What is the probability of three separate spins landing first on green, then on blue, then on red?

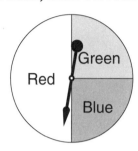

Green

Red

Blue

A $\frac{1}{32}$

B $\frac{3}{32}$

C $\frac{3}{10}$

D 1

4. Of the beads shaped like cubes and spheres, how many necklaces of 3 beads can be made?

A 10   C 40

B 15   D 336

5. Find the value of *d* in the parallelogram.

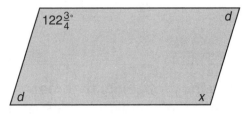

122¾° ... *d*

d ... *x*

A $28\frac{5}{8}°$

B $57\frac{1}{4}°$

C $114\frac{1}{2}°$

D $122\frac{3}{4}°$

---

6. This stem-and-leaf plot shows the number of points Jeanine scored in the first 15 games of the basketball season. How does the median change if she scores 18 points in the next game?

Points Scored by Jeanine

Stem	Leaf
3	0
2	0 1 2 2 5 6 8
1	0 2 5 6 8
0	8 9

A The median increases.

B The median decreases.

C The median stays the same.

D The new data set has no median.

---

7. These puzzle pieces remain in a box. If Taylor picks a piece at random, what is the probability she will pick a quadrilateral?

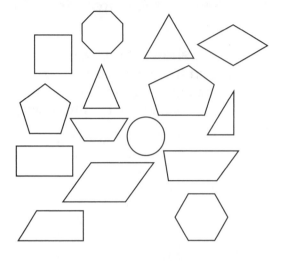

A $\frac{2}{5}$ **C** $\frac{7}{15}$

B $\frac{2}{3}$ **D** $\frac{14}{15}$

---

8. Four congruent square carpet pieces are arranged in a square on the floor—red, blue, green, and yellow. A coin is dropped from directly above the center of the four pieces. What is the probability the coin will land on the yellow piece?

2 ft

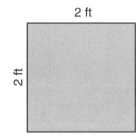

2 ft

A $\frac{1}{16}$

B $\frac{1}{4}$

C $\frac{1}{6}$

D Not enough information given

Read the questions. Use the strategies to choose
the answer choice that makes the most sense.

STRATEGIES

1. **The ratio of fifth graders to sixth graders is 3 to 4. Find an equivalent ratio for 3 to 4.**

   A 10 to 16

   B 14 to 18

   C 15 to 20

   D 21 to 26

   Remember: **Equivalent ratios** have the same value and can be written as **equivalent fractions**.

   • Write the given ratio as a fraction.

   $$\frac{3}{4} \leftarrow \text{fifth graders} \atop \leftarrow \text{sixth graders}$$

   • Multiply or divide both the numerator and the denominator by the same nonzero number. Express the result as a fraction.

   $$\frac{3 \times ?}{4 \times ?} = \frac{3 \times 5}{4 \times 5} = \frac{15}{20}$$

   Since $\frac{3}{4} = \frac{15}{20}$

   Answer choice C is correct.

2. **Barbara ran 24 kilometers at a steady pace in 4 hours. How many kilometers did she run in 1 hour?**

   A 6

   B 8

   C 12

   D 96

   Remember: A **rate** is a ratio that compares two quantities with different units of measure. A **unit rate** is a rate that has 1 unit as its second term, or denominator.

   • To find how many kilometers Barbara ran in 1 hour, x, use equivalent ratios.

   $$\frac{24 \text{ kilometers}}{4 \text{ hours}} = \frac{x \text{ kilometers}}{1 \text{ hour}} \qquad \frac{24 \div 4}{4 \div 4} = \frac{6}{1} \leftarrow \text{unit rate}$$

   Barbara ran 6 kilometers in 1 hour, or 6 kilometers per hour.

   Answer choice A is correct.

3. **Barbara is making costumes for the school play. She knows that 4 costumes will require 16 yd of fabric. How many yards of fabric will she need for 10 costumes?**

   A 10 yd   **C** 30 yd

   B 12 yd   **D** 40 yd

   • Set up a proportion with the information in the problem.

   $$\frac{4}{16} = \frac{10}{y}$$

   • Write the cross products. Then multiply.

   $$\frac{4}{16} = \frac{10}{y}$$
   $$4 \times y = 16 \times 10 \leftarrow 4y = 160$$

   • Solve for the variable.

   $$4y = 160$$
   $$\frac{4y}{4} = \frac{160}{4}$$
   $$y = 40$$

   Answer choice D is correct.

Circle the letter of the correct answer choice.

---

4. A soccer team has 12 boys and 9 girls. What is the ratio of girls to the total number of team members?

  A $\frac{3}{7}$ **C** $\frac{3}{4}$

  B $\frac{4}{7}$ **D** $\frac{7}{3}$

---

5. Find the missing term to form a proportion.

$$\frac{12}{54} = \frac{n}{9}$$

  A 1

  B 2

  C 6

  D 108

---

6. Movies are filmed as a series of pictures called frames. Usually movies are shown at a rate of 24 frames per second. How many frames are in 8 seconds of a movie?

  A 3

  B 8

  C 162

  D 192

---

7. Find the unit rate.
135 miles in 3 hours

  A 45 miles in 1 hour

  B 52 miles in 1 hour

  C 54 miles in 1 hour

  D 68 miles in 1 hour

---

8. Use the unit price to complete:

| $6.50 for 1 hour |
| _____ for 15 hours |

  A $8.50

  B $12.50

  C $97.50

  D $101.50

---

9. Which pair of ratios forms a proportion?

  A $\frac{2}{8}, \frac{6}{16}$

  B $\frac{21}{14}, \frac{3}{2}$

  C $\frac{3}{7}, \frac{14}{18}$

  D $\frac{11}{24}, \frac{15}{36}$

---

10. Which proportion could you use to solve this problem?

> A worker earns $100 every 8 hours. How much would the worker earn in 28 hours?

  A $\frac{8}{28} = \frac{m}{100}$

  B $\frac{8}{100} = \frac{m}{28}$

  C $\frac{8}{100} = \frac{28}{m}$

  D $\frac{100}{28} = \frac{m}{8}$

Read the questions. Use the strategies to choose the answer choice that makes the most sense.

1. **Triangle *CAT* is similar to Triangle *DOG*. What is the length of *n*?**

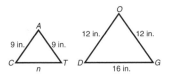

   A 6.75 in. **C** 12 in.

   B 9 in. **D** 16 in.

- Write a proportion.

$$\frac{CA}{DO} = \frac{CT}{DG} \rightarrow \frac{9}{12} = \frac{n}{16}$$

- Use cross products to solve.

$$12 \times n = 9 \times 16$$
$$12n = 144$$
$$12n \div 12 = 144 \div 12n$$
$$n = 12$$

Answer choice C is correct.

---

2. **Robert is 6 ft tall. His shadow is 15 ft long. He is standing near a vertical flagpole that casts a 75 ft shadow. How tall is the flagpole?**

   A 15 ft **C** 90 ft

   B 30 ft **D** 187.5 ft

To find the height of the flagpole, *h*, draw a pair of similar right triangles. Then write and solve a proportion.

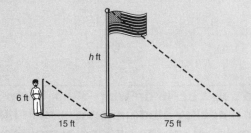

$$\frac{6 \text{ ft}}{15 \text{ ft}} = \frac{h \text{ ft}}{75 \text{ ft}} \leftarrow \text{Write a proportion.}$$
$$6 \times 75 = 15h \leftarrow \text{Use the cross products rule.}$$
$$450 \div 15 = 15h \div 15 \leftarrow \text{Apply the Division Property of Equality}$$
$$30 = h$$

The flagpole is 30 ft tall.

Answer choice B is correct.

---

3. **A map uses a scale in which 1 inch represents 6 miles. What distance is represented by $3\frac{1}{2}$ inches?**

   A $\frac{1}{2}$ miles **C** 10 miles

   B $7\frac{1}{2}$ miles **D** 21 miles

- Write a proportion that compares map distance to actual distance. Use the scale as one side of the proportion. Use the actual distance represented by $3\frac{1}{2}$ in. as the other side of the proportion.

Scale	Distance You Want to Find

$$\frac{\text{map}}{\text{actual}} \rightarrow \frac{1 \text{ in.}}{6 \text{ mi.}} = \frac{3\frac{1}{2} \text{ in.}}{n} \leftarrow \frac{\text{map}}{\text{actual}}$$

- You can use cross products to solve a proportion.

$$\frac{1}{6} = \frac{3\frac{1}{2}}{n} \rightarrow 1 \times n = 6 \times 3\frac{1}{2} \rightarrow n = \textbf{21 miles}$$

Answer choice D is correct.

Circle the letter of the correct answer choice.

4. Rectangle *JUMP* is similar to rectangle *SKIP*. The lengths of the sides are measured in inches. Find the length of segment *PI*.

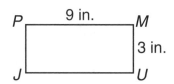

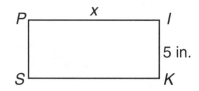

A 5.4 in.   C 15 in.

B 11 in.   D 17 in.

5. Jose has a scale drawing of his favorite team's hockey stadium on a card in his wallet. What are the dimensions of the real hockey rink?

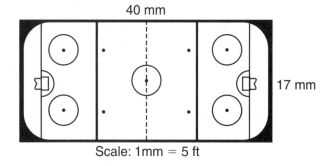

Scale: 1mm = 5 ft

A 8 feet × 3.4 feet

B 34 feet × 80 feet

C 40 feet × 17 feet

D 85 feet × 200 feet

6. Raul sees that a 12-ft telephone pole is casting an 18-ft shadow at the same time he is casting a 6-ft shadow. How tall is Raul?

A 4 feet   C 24 feet

B 9 feet   D 36 feet

7. Use the map below to answer the question. Measure the scale distance on the map to the nearest 0.5 cm.

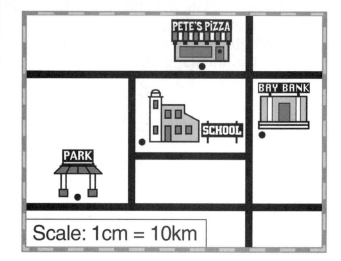

How many miles is it from Pete's Pizza to Bay Bank?

A 2.5 km

B 4 km

C 10 km

D 25 km

8. The lengths, in inches, of the sides of a rectangle are 57 and 87. If the shorter sides of a similar rectangle are 19 feet long, how long are its longer sides?

A 12 in.   C 29 in.

B 18 in.   D 57 in.

Read the questions. Use the strategies to choose
the answer choice that makes the most sense.

STRATEGIES

1. Rename $\frac{9}{25}$ **as a percent.**

   A 25%

   B 36%

   C 75%

   D 133%

• Write a proportion, using $\frac{9}{25}$ and $\frac{n}{100}$ as the ratios.

$$\frac{9}{25} = \frac{n}{100}$$

> Remember: percent means "per hundred" or "out of 100."

• Use cross products to solve. Write the percent symbol next to the value of n.

$$\frac{9}{25} = \frac{n}{100}$$
$$9 \times 100 = 25 \times n$$
$$900 \div 25 = 25n \div 25$$
$$36 = n$$

So, $\frac{9}{25} = 36\%$

Answer choice B is correct.

2. Which answer choice correctly orders the numbers from least to greatest?

$$0.65, \frac{1}{50}, 90\%, \frac{1}{2}$$

   A 90%, 0.65, $\frac{1}{50}, \frac{1}{2}$

   B 90%, 0.65, $\frac{1}{2}, \frac{1}{50}$

   C $\frac{1}{50}, \frac{1}{2}$, 0.65, 90%

   D $\frac{1}{2}, \frac{1}{50}$, 90%, 0.65

• Rename all the rational numbers and percents as fractions.

$$0.65 = \frac{65}{100}; \frac{1}{50} = \frac{2}{100}; 90\% = \frac{90}{100}; \frac{1}{2} = \frac{50}{100}$$

• Order the fractions.

$$\frac{2}{100}, \frac{50}{100}, \frac{65}{100}, \frac{90}{100}$$

Answer choice C is correct.

3. A stock increases 0.46% during a week of trading. What is this change written as an equivalent decimal and an equivalent fraction?

   A 0.0046, $\frac{23}{5000}$ **C** 4.6, $\frac{23}{50}$

   B 0.046, $\frac{46}{1000}$ **D** 46, $\frac{23}{5000}$

• Write the percent as a decimal.

$$0.46\% = 0.46 \div 100 = 0.0046$$

> **Think**
> A percent less than 1% is equivalent to a decimal less than 0.01.

• Write the decimal as a fraction. Simplify.

$$0.0046 = \frac{46}{10,000} = \frac{23}{5000}$$

Answer choice A is correct.

Circle the letter of the correct answer choice.

4. At Mr. Ramirez's store, 64% of the fruit sold is bananas. Express this as a fraction in simplest form.

A $\frac{25}{12}$

B $\frac{64}{100}$

C $\frac{32}{50}$

D $\frac{16}{25}$

5. Which fraction is equivalent to 0.5%?

A $\frac{1}{2}$

B $\frac{1}{20}$

C $\frac{1}{50}$

D $\frac{1}{200}$

6. Which answer choice orders the numbers from least to greatest?

$$153\%, 19\%, 0.8, \frac{1}{50}, 1.5$$

A $\frac{1}{50}$, 1.5, 153%, 0.8, 19%

B $\frac{1}{50}$, 19%, 0.8, 1.5, 153%

C 153%, 1.5, 0.8, 19%, $\frac{1}{50}$

D $\frac{1}{50}$, 0.8, 1.5, 19%, 153%

7. The attendance at baseball games is 125% higher than it was ten years ago. What decimal is this?

A 12.5

B 0.125

C 1.25

D 0.0125

8. What is $\frac{4}{7}$ expressed as a percent?

A $57\frac{1}{2}\%$

B $57\frac{1}{7}\%$

C $67\frac{1}{8}\%$

D $68\frac{1}{7}\%$

9. It rained on 56% of the days in April. Which answer choice shows 56% as a decimal?

A 0.056

B 0.56

C 5.6

D 56

10. Which percent is equivalent to $\frac{5}{8}$?

A 58%

B $62\frac{1}{2}\%$

C 75%

D 160%